Praise for
EMDR Workbook for Kids

"Through unique and playful worksheets and exercises, Christine Mark-Griffin has transformed the complex and layered therapeutic approach of EMDR into a kid-friendly, accessible, and lighthearted one that is much less daunting for littles. Practicing EMDR with children has never been easier thanks to the *EMDR Workbook for Kids*!"

 —**Christina Furnival, LPC,** author of *The Not-So-Friendly Friend* and *Fear Not!*

"The *EMDR Workbook for Kids* is a must-read for every EMDR therapist who helps children overcome trauma, stress, or other emotional issues. With a comprehensive, relational approach and a user-friendly writing style, Christine Mark-Griffin covers everything you need to know (and more!) to take your child-focused EMDR practice to the next level."

 —**Rotem Brayer, MEd, LPC,** author of *The Art and Science of EMDR*

"My advice over the years to EMDR clinicians trying to adapt it for children has been: 'Make it visual and playful, and use simpler and more engaging words.' In this *EMDR Workbook for Kids*, Christine Mark-Griffin has done just that. She takes away the guesswork and offers a busy EMDR child therapist a ready-made tool. The artwork is so appealing, and the language is very comfortable and comprehensible for children while being faithful to the protocol in every detail. I would strongly encourage especially newly trained EMDR clinicians to hurry out and get this resource right away!"

 —**Ann Beckley-Forest, LCSW-R, RPT-S,** EMDR approved consultant and trainer

"When child therapists finish their basic EMDR training, they are looking for guidance on how to implement the protocol with children. Christine Mark-Griffin provides a simple and easy-to-understand workbook that offers the guidance every child therapist needs to effectively deliver the eight phases in a developmentally appropriate manner. Christine uses the language of play through her kid-friendly scripts and worksheets that make it easy to work through each phase with a child. This workbook helps therapists with staying true to the protocol and doing it in a way that works for kids of all ages."

 —**Annie J. Monaco, LCSW-R, RPT-S,** EMDR approved consultant and trainer

EMDR Workbook for Kids

A Collection of EMDR Handouts & Worksheets to Help Kids Process Trauma, Stress, Anger, Sadness & More

eye movement desensitization & reprocessing

Christine Mark-Griffin, LCSW

Disclaimer: This workbook is intended for use by qualified, EMDR-trained clinicians as a supplement to EMDR therapy. Clinicians who use this workbook should not practice outside of their own areas of competency. This workbook is not a replacement for EMDR therapy or appropriate EMDR training.

Published by
PESI Publishing, Inc.
3839 White Ave
Eau Claire, WI 54703

Cover Design: Emily Dyer
Editing: Jenessa Jackson, PhD
Layout: Emily Dyer

ISBN: 9781683735854 (print)
ISBN: 9781683735861 (KPF)
ISBN: 9781683735878 (ePDF)

PESI Publishing
pesipublishing.com

About the Author

Christine Mark-Griffin, LCSW, is a certified EMDR therapist and EMDRIA-approved consultant. She is the owner of Spark All Wellness, a private practice specializing in EMDR therapy with children, EMDR consultation for clinicians, and trauma-informed trainings for professional organizations. Christine started her social work career in child protective services and later transitioned to school-based mental health, where she was a clinical supervisor and trainer. Christine lectures at California State University, Monterey Bay, where she teaches undergraduate courses in abnormal child psychology. Christine lives in San Francisco with her husband, two children, and dog. The things that make her happiest include her family and friends, a good cup of coffee, baked goods, yoga, traveling, cycling, music, and dancing.

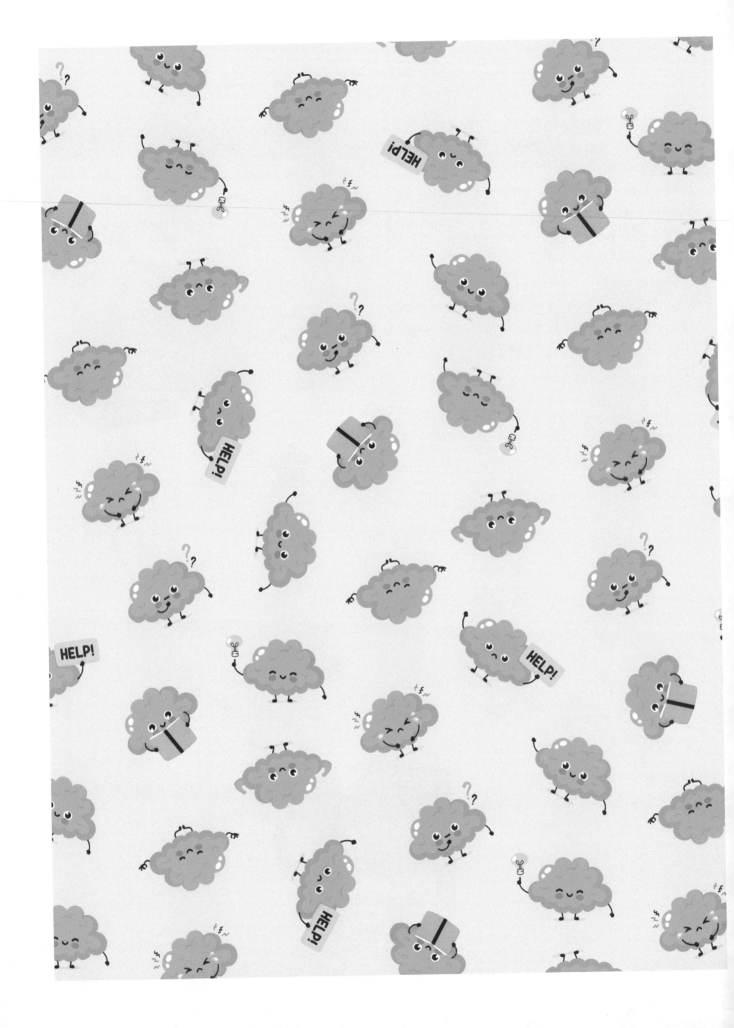

Table of Contents

A Letter to Therapists

Dear EMDR child therapist,

I hope you know how wonderful you are. Every day, I am so inspired by the tremendous healing and life-changing work we get to witness through EMDR therapy. The work you do is truly magical.

Since you are reading this book, I am assuming that you are no stranger to working with children and families who are highly traumatized. You may relate to being asked questions like "Isn't that hard? Isn't it depressing? How do you do it?" from people who aren't in a similar field. To be honest, I have had my fair share of moments where I asked myself these same questions.

The reality is, it's really hard some days to work in this field! Like many of you, I have an entire library of painful and devastating stories that little ones have shared with me over the years. For me, holding these stories and attempting to do traditional therapy with these kids was not enough. In my search to find something that could actually help, I discovered eye movement desensitization and reprocessing (EMDR).

My basic training for EMDR was predominately geared toward adults, with only a tiny section addressing EMDR with children. In my search for more, I tried to find child-friendly EMDR visuals—and to my surprise, I had no luck! Here is where my journey began in creating EMDR worksheets and visuals for children.

Over time, I developed a comprehensive collection of these worksheets, and I am so proud and honored to share it with you. I hope this workbook will inspire you to playfully integrate EMDR therapy into your practice with children while remaining true to the integrity and core components of EMDR. You should only use this workbook if you are an EMDR-trained clinician and are searching for supplemental tools to enhance your therapeutic work with children.

The first eight sections in this workbook correspond with the eight phases of EMDR therapy. In each section, you will find visual handouts, worksheets, activities, and ideas to engage elementary-aged children in EMDR therapy. In the last section, you will find helpful handouts for parents and caregivers. You may choose to complete the workbook from start to finish or select specific worksheets to complete with your child clients. Some worksheets can also be used to track children's progress throughout treatment. You may choose to have the children complete the worksheets on their own or together with you or their caregivers. The options are endless!

Working with children has many challenges, but it is both essential and rewarding. Let's fill up your toolbox and help you spark some creativity, playfulness, imagination, laughter, and fun with the little ones who enter your therapy office.

With gratitude and playfulness,

Christine Mark-Griffin, LCSW

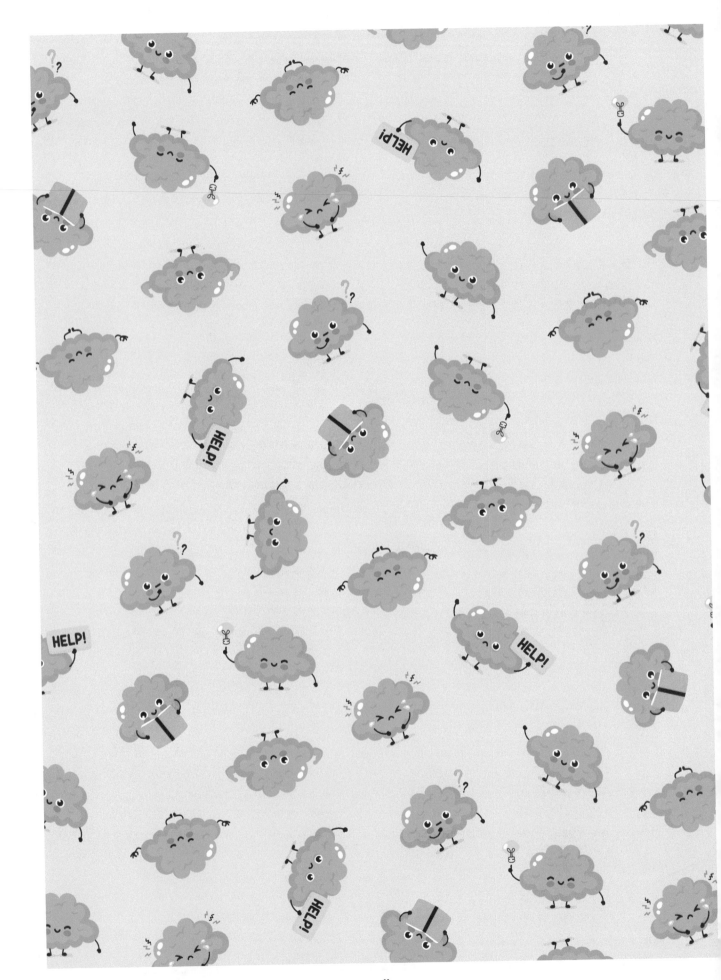

Introduction

What Is EMDR Therapy?

Eye movement desensitization and reprocessing therapy (or EMDR therapy, for short!) is a type of therapy that can help kids and grown-ups feel better after scary, stressful, or traumatic experiences. It can help you work through big emotions you might be feeling, like worry, sadness, and anger, as well as any unhelpful thoughts or memories that you can't seem to get out of your mind. It can also help you process uncomfortable body sensations, like feeling shaky, having a funny feeling in your stomach, or feeling hot in certain parts of your body.

How Does EMDR Therapy Work?

When a painful or upsetting experience happens, the memory of that experience sometimes stays "stuck" in your body, heart, and mind (Shapiro, 2018). An EMDR therapist can help you figure out what memories are getting stuck and giving you problems. In EMDR therapy, you will be asked to focus on these upsetting memories while using back-and-forth movements to help your brain and body get unstuck. There are lots of ways to do back-and-forth movements in EMDR. The most common types include moving your eyes, tapping with your hands, marching your feet, using buzzers, or listening to sounds in an alternating left-right pattern. These movements are all types of bilateral stimulation—meaning that they light up both sides of your brain and body.

What Does EMDR Therapy Help With?

EMDR therapy can help kids feel better about a bunch of different problems:

- ⭐ Bullying
- ⭐ Anxiety and worries
- ⭐ Sadness
- ⭐ Anger problems
- ⭐ Parents arguing and fighting

- ⭐ Parents divorcing or separating
- ⭐ Medical problems
- ⭐ Moving to a new country
- ⭐ Eating issues
- ⭐ Losing a person or pet
- ⭐ Experiencing abuse (physical, emotional, sexual) or neglect
- ⭐ Nightmares
- ⭐ Sleeping problems
- ⭐ Witnessing violence in your neighborhood
- ⭐ Experiencing natural disasters, like earthquakes, fires, or tornadoes
- ⭐ And much more!

If you have experienced one or more of these problems and are having a hard time right now, know that you are not alone—and EMDR can help. Your EMDR therapist will work with you and your caregivers to figure out how to help you feel better. Let's get started by learning more about the story of EMDR, and then we'll learn more about your story.

A Story of EMDR Therapy

Once upon a time, a psychologist and researcher named Francine Shapiro discovered that when she moved her eyes back and forth while thinking about something stressful, she was able to feel much better!

In response to this discovery, she developed a therapy called EMDR, which stands for eye movement desensitization and reprocessing. To understand how EMDR works, it helps to know a little bit about how the brain processes stressful situations.

When something scary or stressful happens, our brains, bodies, and hearts can have a hard time making sense of the experience. Sometimes, the memory of this experience gets stuck in our brains and causes a lot of trouble in the way we think, feel, and act.

Francine figured out that we can use eight phases in EMDR therapy to help our brains and bodies get unstuck and begin healing from those scary and stressful experiences.

Phase 1 My Story and Goals	**Phase 2** Getting Prepared	**Phase 3** Activating Targets	**Phase 4** Discharging the Stress
Phase 5 Strengthening the Positive	**Phase 6** Increasing Body Awareness	**Phase 7** Finishing and Ending	**Phase 8** Reviewing and Revising

In EMDR therapy, you will focus on your scary or stressful experience while doing back-and-forth movements, known as bilateral stimulation, to help you get unstuck. While Francine initially used eye movements as the main type of bilateral stimulation, there are many types of back-and-forth movements that are effective, including tapping your hands, listening to sounds, marching your feet, or using buzzers in a left-right pattern.

With EMDR therapy, Francine figured out how to help people get unstuck from stressful experiences and feel better in their hearts, bodies, and minds. That's pretty cool!

Reference: Shapiro (2018)

What Are the Phases of EMDR Therapy?

EMDR therapy has eight phases to help your body, heart, and mind get unstuck from scary and traumatic memories that have become trapped in your brain (Shapiro, 2018). The eight phases are:

1. Your Story and Goals
2. Getting Prepared
3. Activating Targets
4. Discharging the Stress
5. Strengthening the Positive
6. Increasing Body Awareness
7. Finishing and Ending
8. Reviewing and Revising

Let's walk through each of these phases so you know what to expect!

The 8 Phases of EMDR Therapy

Phase 1
My Story and Goals

During phase 1 of EMDR, you will work on sharing your story and figuring out the parts of your story that are causing problems for you. Once you figure out the problems you would like to work on, you will work with your EMDR therapist to come up with goals to help with those problems.

Phase 2
Getting Prepared

During phase 2, you will work on building trust with your EMDR therapist and learn the basics of how EMDR works. You will also learn new skills to calm down and cope with uncomfortable feelings and emotions that might show up during EMDR therapy.

Phase 3
Activating Targets

In phase 3, you will work with your therapist to identify (1) a target problem, (2) an image that comes to mind when you think of the problem, (3) unhelpful thoughts, (4) helpful thoughts, (5) how true the helpful thought feels, (6) the emotions you feel, (7) how stressed out this problem makes you feel, and (8) where you feel the stress in your body.

Phase 4
Discharging the Stress

In phase 4, you will focus on the target problem while doing some type of back-and-forth movement with your EMDR therapist. These movements can include moving your eyes, tapping your hands, drawing, dancing, and much more! The goal of phase 4 is to help you move and shake the stress of the target problem out of your body, heart, and mind.

Phase 5
Strengthening
the Positive

Phase 5 is where you will focus on strengthening your positive and healthy thoughts so that whenever you are reminded or think about your target problem in the future, you won't feel stressed out. For example, instead of thinking, "I'm not safe," you will think, "I'm safe now!"

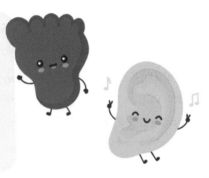

Phase 6
Increasing
Body
Awareness

In phase 6, you will work with your EMDR therapist to release any unhelpful memories that are stuck in your body. If you notice any uncomfortable feelings in your body, let your EMDR therapist know so you can keep doing back-and-forth movements to release the stress from your body!

Phase 7
Finishing
and Ending

All EMDR sessions will finish and end in the same way: by doing something calming or fun. Your therapist will also talk to you about what to expect in between sessions.

Phase 8
Reviewing
and Revising

At the beginning of each EMDR session, your therapist will see if your problem has gotten better or worse since the last session, including any triggers that might have come up for you. You will see if your target problem has been solved or talk about things you still need to work on.

Reference: Shapiro (2018)

The Process of EMDR Therapy

During EMDR therapy, you may stay in one or more phases for a while before you are ready to move on to the next phase. For example, you might be in phase 2 for a while to get super prepared and ready for the rest of the phases. You will also probably repeat some phases a couple of times. For instance, you might go through phases 3 through 8 a bunch of times for the same target problem or for different target problems you are experiencing. You might also circle back to some phases in EMDR—like in the diagram below—and that's okay! There is no right or wrong order of how you go through the phases of EMDR.

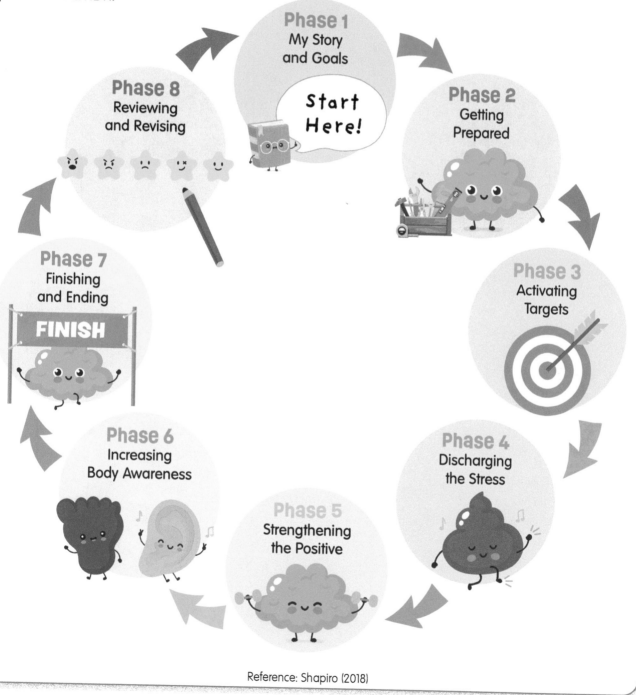

Reference: Shapiro (2018)

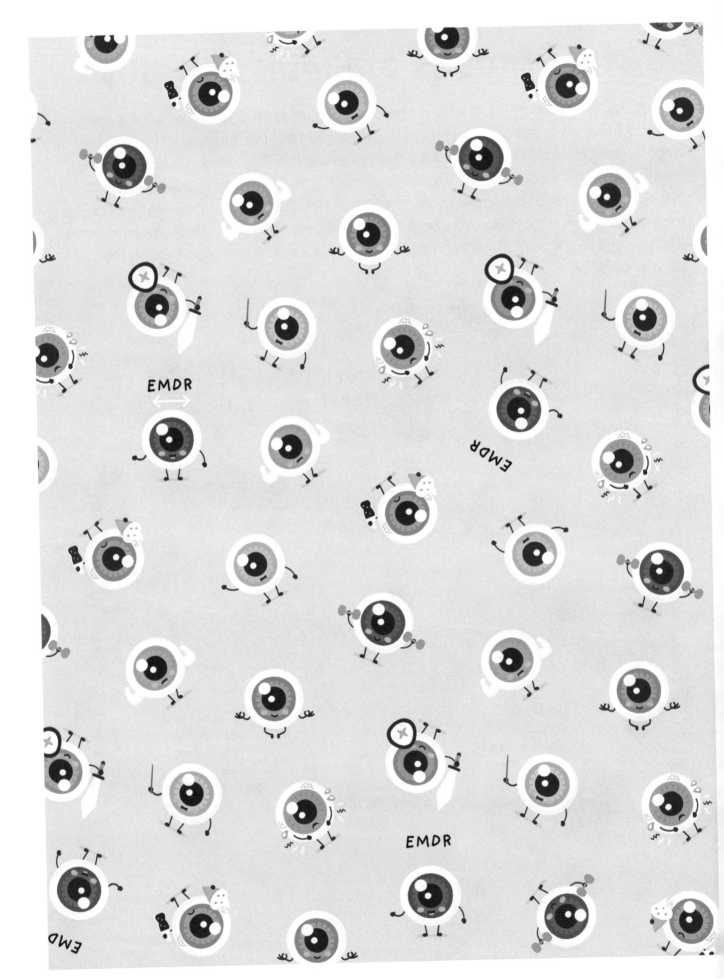

CHAPTER 1

PHASE 1: My Story and Goals

Now that you are more familiar with the story and process of EMDR therapy, let's learn about your story and goals.

That's what phase 1 of EMDR therapy is all about—learning your story and creating goals to help you feel better! Francine Shapiro calls this the "client history taking and treatment planning" phase. We will spend time collecting information about the problems you are experiencing and make a plan to help these problems go away. You will work with your therapist to figure out the events, experiences, memories, or problems that you wish to "target" with EMDR. In EMDR therapy, this is called the "target memory" or "target problem." Once you figure out what target memories and problems you would like to work on, your therapist will help you create a plan and set some goals!

Clinician Tip: Consider using the handouts in chapter 9 to simultaneously gather information from the child and their caregivers. Some children may be able to share their story and set their goals independently, while others may need additional assistance from the supportive adults in their life.

Phase 1: My Story and Goals

Phase 1 is all about exploring your story, including the parts that are troubling you, and using this knowledge to set your goals for EMDR therapy. You and your therapist will do this by following three steps.

Step 1:
Learning About Your Story

You will be asked to share your favorite memories and the scary or traumatic memories that are bothering you.

Step 2:
Figuring Out the Target Problems or Memories in Your Story

You will decide which problems or memories bug you the most.

Step 3:
Making a Plan and Setting Goals

Your EMDR therapist will help you create a plan and set some goals that will help you start feeling better!

Reference: Shapiro (2018)

My Story Worksheet

Once upon a time, there was a child named _____. This child was _____ years
(Your name)   (Your age)

old and lived with _____ in _____.
(Whom do you live with?)   (Where do you live?)

This child's favorite color was _____ and their favorite thing to
(Favorite color)

eat was _____. The thing this child had the most fun doing
(Favorite food)

was _____.
(Make a list of things you like to do for fun)

This child has had a lot of good things happen in their life. Some of the best memories this

child can remember where they felt really happy include: _____,
(1st best memory)

_____,
(2nd best memory)

_____ , and
(3rd best memory)

_____.
(4th best memory)

While this child has had a lot of good experiences and memories, they have also had some

bad, scary, and upsetting things happen to them. These bad and scary things are so upsetting

that this child can't seem to stop thinking about these bad memories. They feel like they are

stuck in this child's mind. The bad memories include: _____,
(1st bad memory)

_____ , and
(2nd bad memory)

_____.
(3rd bad memory)

Sometimes, these bad memories and experiences can cause a lot of problems for this child,

such as: _____.
(Make a list of the problems these memories are causing, like getting angry, having trouble sleeping, or worrying too much)

Even though these memories have been giving this child a lot of problems right now, they are

working hard to get rid of these problems so that in the future they can _____

_____.
(Write about what it will be like in the future for you when you no longer have these problems)

Comic Strips Story

In the comic strips below, create stories about your happiest memories, your scariest memories, and other memories that make you feel upset so that we can learn more about your story. You can make copies of this page to create multiple memories or gather your own materials to make your comic strips. Let's get creative!

Below is an example of a comic strip for a scary memory.

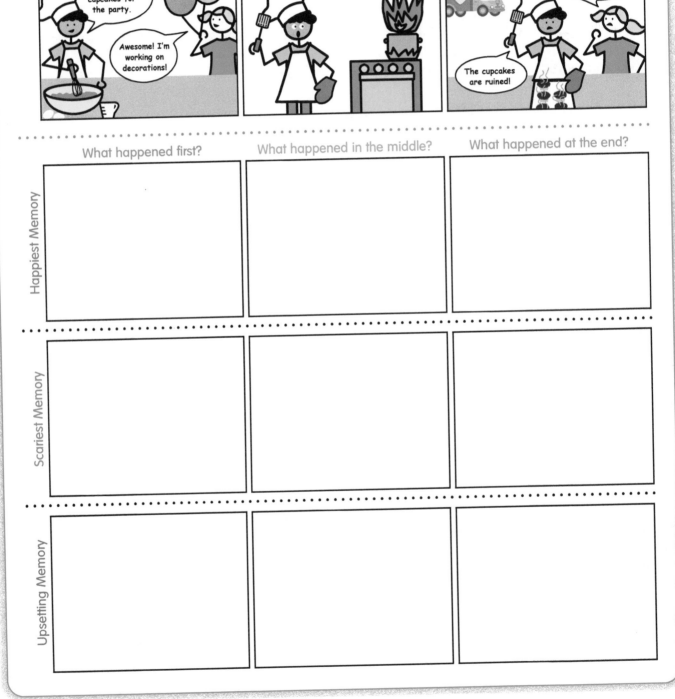

My Favorite Memories

Let's learn about some of your favorite memories! In each bubble, draw a symbol or write a couple of words to help you remember a special, positive day or moment that you've had. Do you have a favorite place you have visited? A favorite holiday? A favorite day or party that you remember?

WHAT ARE SOME OF YOUR
FAVORITE POSITIVE MEMORIES
THAT ARE IN YOUR BRAIN?

My Scary, Confusing, Traumatic Memories

Sometimes, our brains get confusing, scary, and traumatic memories stuck inside them. In the bubbles, write or draw some upsetting memories that have gotten stuck for you. These can be memories that have been stuck for a very long time or new memories that have just gotten stuck.

WHAT ARE THE SCARY, CONFUSING, OR TRAUMATIC MEMORIES IN YOUR BRAIN?

Common Target Problems

Before we can start making a plan about how to solve your problems, we need to know what types of problems are giving you trouble. Below are some common problems that many kids have. Put a check mark by any examples that are problems for you, or add some problems in the blank spaces if you do not see your problem listed.

☐ Nightmares   ☐ Becoming aggressive

☐ Flashbacks   ☐ Feeling on edge

☐ Trouble sleeping   ☐ Having bad thoughts about myself

☐ Becoming startled   ☐ Avoiding people or places

☐ Feeling angry   ☐ Not having fun anymore

☐ Feeling annoyed   ☐ Finding it hard to concentrate

☐ Feeling worried   ☐ Having a hard time feeling happy

☐ Feeling sad   ☐ Blaming myself or others

☐ Feeling scared   ☐ Isolating from people

☐ Feeling numb   ☐ Trouble eating

☐ _____   ☐ _____

☐ _____   ☐ _____

☐ _____   ☐ _____

Past, Present, Future

Draw or write about a scary or upsetting event that has happened to you in the "past" circle. Next, draw or write about how this event is still giving you problems today in the "present" circle. Finally, in the "future" circle, draw or write about how you would like things to be in the future when this memory no longer bothers you.

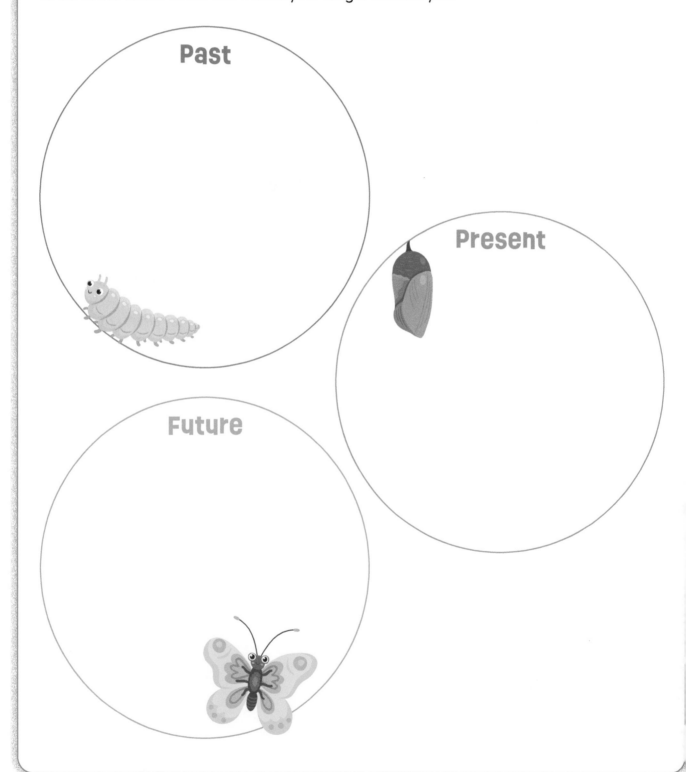

Making a Plan

Let's make a plan to help you with some of the problems you are experiencing. Write or draw in the boxes below to begin making a plan.

 What is your target problem?

 What unhelpful thoughts do you get when you have this problem?

 How do you behave when you have this problem?

 What are the helpful thoughts you would like to have instead?

 How would you like to behave instead?

Can you think of a list of people who can help you with this problem at home or school? (e.g., parent, grandparent, teacher, friend, sibling, pet, neighbor, babysitter, coach, aunt, or uncle)

Setting My Goals

Use this worksheet to help you set some goals for EMDR therapy!

What are your top three goals for EMDR therapy?

Goal 1	Goal 2	Goal 3

Who can help you reach your goals? Draw or write the names of people who can help you.

Person 1	Person 2	Person 3

What steps can you take to reach your goals? Write them below.

Step 1	Step 2	Step 3

How will you know when you have reached your goal? Write or draw this below.

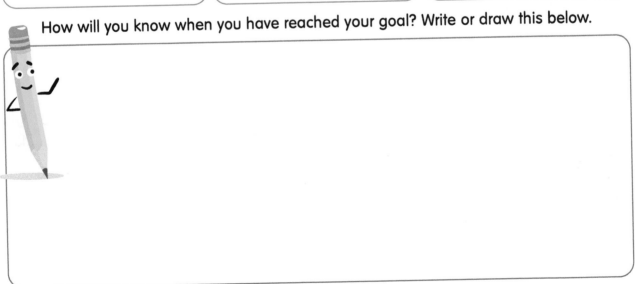

CHAPTER 2

PHASE 2: Getting Prepared

During phase 2 of EMDR, which Francine Shapiro calls the "preparation phase," we will focus on building trust and learn more about how EMDR therapy works. A good way to understand EMDR therapy is to imagine that your brain is a road or a highway. When the information in your brain can get from point A to point B, you can process your thoughts, emotions, and body sensations in a healthy manner.

But when the road becomes blocked, it can be hard to get to point B safely and on time. You may take a detour, try a different route, get lost, or even end up somewhere you really don't want to be. When your brain cannot reach its final destination due to these roadblocks, you may process your experiences and memories in an unhealthy way.

EMDR therapy can help you figure out what your roadblocks are, understand how they got there, and remove those blocks so you can make it to your destination safe and sound. To do so, you will learn about some different types of back-and-forth movements that can help you unblock the road and think more positively about the scary or upsetting event that happened to you.

Your EMDR therapist will also help you learn more about your emotions and how you respond when you feel unsafe, stressed, or overwhelmed. You'll learn about your body's built-in alarm system that triggers you to fight, take flight, or freeze when you feel threatened (Cannon, 1915). Finally, you will learn a bunch of coping skills you can use when things get hard. This way, when you begin EMDR therapy, you will feel prepared to handle any difficult emotions or reactions you might experience during or between sessions.

Let's get this show on the road!

Clinician Tip: Consider which worksheets and activities in the preparation phase can be completed jointly with the child and their caregiver. You may choose to include the caregiver in the session as you introduce certain handouts, such as *Learning Back-and-Forth Movements*. You may even have the child and caregiver practice doing back-and-forth movements together during the session. You can also have the child and caregiver practice coping and calming skills for homework by having them complete *Safe, Calm Place* or *Breathing Shift* together outside of session.

Roadblocks in the Brain

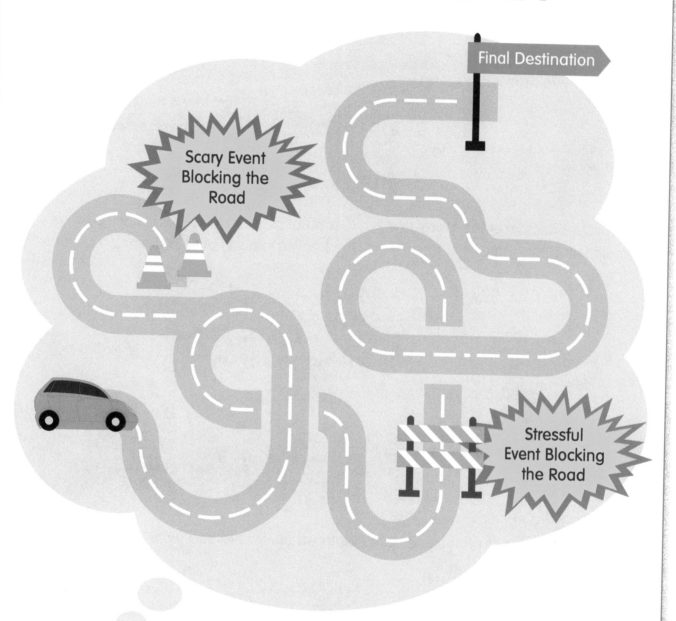

Final Destination

Scary Event Blocking the Road

Stressful Event Blocking the Road

When we are stuck in traffic, it can be really hard to get to our final destination. Let's imagine your brain is a road, and stressful or scary events have caused roadblocks. When you have too many roadblocks, it can cause a traffic jam in your brain and create all sorts of problems! It's important for the roads in your brain to get unblocked because your brain is processing a lot of information each day!

Removing the Roadblocks

Every day, your brain is processing and storing all kinds of information.

When your brain becomes overwhelmed from scary or stressful events, it can't process information in the same way, and the natural healing powers of your brain can become blocked.

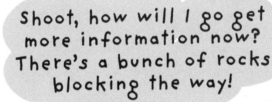

EMDR therapy can help you figure out what those blocks are and work to remove those blocks so your brain can heal.

Reference: Shapiro (2018)

Rebuilding the Road

When there are too many scary or confusing events that cause roadblocks in the brain, you can get really stuck!

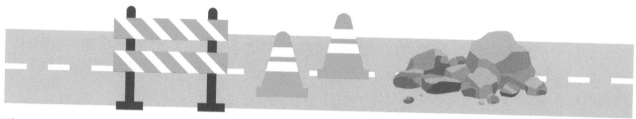

These scary or confusing things can make you feel really bad.

In EMDR therapy, we will focus on these scary events while using back-and-forth movements at the same time to help unblock the road!

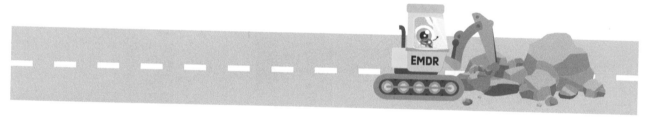

Once the road is unblocked and repaired, it will be easier to feel and think more positively about yourself and the scary or confusing things that have happened.

You are the boss in EMDR therapy! You will get to decide when you want to stop and when you need to take a break. Removing roadblocks and rebuilding roads in the brain can be really hard work!

Wow! I'm tired after all that hard work!

Reference: Shapiro (2018)

Learning Back-and-Forth Movements

There are many types of back-and-forth movements that can be effective in helping you unblock the road. Below are some common movements that many people use in EMDR. Try to practice each one to see what kind of movement you like the most. You may also discover and learn other back-and-forth movements with your EMDR therapist that you can use.

 Move your eyes back and forth. Your EMDR therapist can help you learn different directions to move your eyes.

 Stand up and march in place to create back-and-forth movement with your legs and feet.

 Using your hand, scribble back and forth on a piece of paper with a crayon, marker, or pencil. Follow your hand with your eyes as you scribble.

 Use musical instruments such as drums or shakers to create back-and-forth movements.

 Tap back and forth on different parts of your body. Try tapping on your head, shoulders, knees, and toes!

 Hula hoop and use your hips and whole body to make back-and-forth movements!

 Jump up and down or side to side to create back-and-forth movement!

 Play pat-a-cake with your EMDR therapist, parent, or caregiver to create back-and-forth movement with your hands.

 Listen to sounds or music that move back and forth from one ear to the other.

 Use TheraTappers or "Buzzies" that vibrate back and forth with your EMDR therapist.

Create your own back-and-forth movement! Write or draw it below.

Create your own back-and-forth movement! Write or draw it below.

Reference: Shapiro (2018)

Alarm System

Did you know that our brains and bodies have a built-in alarm system? This system helps us detect danger and survive. It is similar to the fire alarm that you may have at home or school. When the fire alarm detects a fire, it turns on to warn you that you are in danger.

When the alarm in your brain and body goes off, your stress responses turn on to help your body fight, take flight, or freeze. Below are examples of how these stress responses might feel or look. Circle the examples that happen to you the most.

Fight

Feels like:

Angry
Frustrated
Offended
Aggressive

Looks like:

Hitting
Biting
Yelling
Using mean words
Talking back
Blaming

Flight

Feels like:

Overwhelmed
Anxious
Scared
Worried

Looks like:

Running away
Wanting to leave
Fidgeting
Trouble focusing
Procrastinating
Avoiding the situation

Freeze

Feels like:

Bored
Numb
Zoned out
Helpless

Looks like:

Hiding
Not talking or responding
Shutting down
Wanting to be alone
Spacing out
Daydreaming

False Alarms

From time to time, you may have false alarms that cause your stress response to turn on even when there's no danger, just like birthday candles might accidentally trigger a fire alarm. It is okay to have false alarms every once in a while, but it can become a problem when your brain has too many false alarms.

Let's practice noticing false alarms. For each example below, draw an arrow to help your brain identify whether the situation is a true alarm or a false alarm.

Your teacher asks you to sit down.

A puppy tries to lick you.

You have a hard test at school.

An angry dog is trying to bite you.

You are in a car crash.

Threat Mode and Thrive Mode

When your brain gets activated by false alarms too often, your stress response system turns on too much. This causes you to be in threat mode most of the time, where you're in a state of fight, flight, or freeze.

With practice, you can learn to notice when your mind, heart, and body are in threat mode—even when there's no danger—so you can use calming and coping tools to turn threat mode off. This way, you can turn on thrive mode! In thrive mode, you are not worried about any scary or dangerous situations. Instead, you can spend time living your life, loving yourself and others, and learning new things!

During EMDR therapy, it will be important to notice when your threat mode has been activated. In the beginning of therapy, this mode might be turned on a lot! If this happens, let your therapist know so you can pause, take a break, or stop the EMDR session.

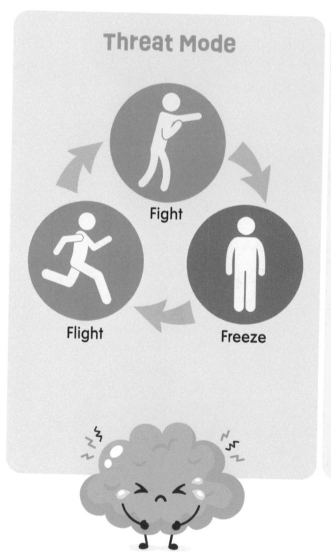

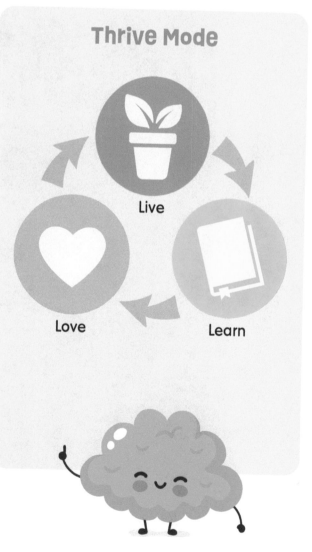

Staying in the Zone

Did you know that you have three different zones, just like a stoplight? EMDR therapy works best when you are in the green zone, meaning that you are good to go—you can handle any hard thoughts, feelings, or body sensations that come up. However, at some points in therapy, you will get into the yellow zone, where it's hard to feel your emotions, or the red zone, where it's hard to handle your emotions. And that's okay. Whenever that happens, it's important to use your stop sign, which lets your therapist know that what you're feeling is too much. You and your therapist can then explore ways to help you calm down, express your feelings, and feel less overwhelmed. Let's learn more about the stoplight zones and how you can move between them.

Creating a Stop Sign

In EMDR therapy, you will come up with a "stop sign" that you can use at any time to let your EMDR therapist know that you need to take a break or stop. Use the outline of the stop sign below or your own materials to design your very own stop sign or special signal!

Stoplight Zones

Now that you have created your stop sign, it's a good idea to figure out exactly when you will need to use it. A simple way to know when you need to use your stop sign is to figure out what zone you are in. The stoplight below will help you understand if you are in the right zone to keep going with EMDR therapy or if you might need to take a break or stop for the day.

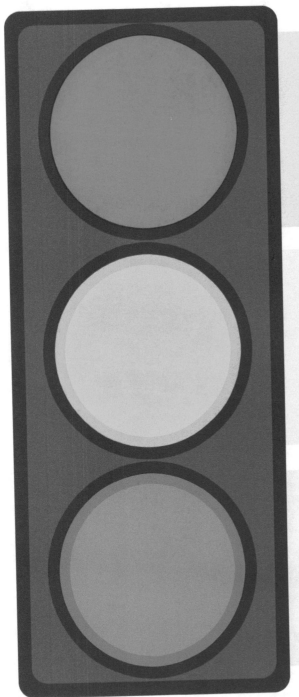

In the **RED** zone, it is hard to handle your emotions and you overrespond with:

- Anger
- Worry
- Panic
- Overwhelm
- Fear
- Shakiness
- Fast breathing
- Too much energy

In the **YELLOW** zone, it is hard to feel your emotions and you feel:

- Numb
- Disconnected
- Far away
- Tired
- Shut down
- Frozen
- Foggy
- Low in energy
- Spaced out

In the **GREEN** zone, you are good to go! You can manage all your emotions (even the uncomfortable ones) while still feeling:

- Present
- Calm
- Playful
- Flexible
- Open
- Curious
- Grounded

This worksheet is original to the author but inspired by numerous sources, including Siegel (1999), Beckley-Forest & Monaco (2021), Gomez (2013), and Kuypers (2011).

Exploring My Stoplight Zones

Now that you know what it looks like in all of the different stoplight zones, let's spend some time thinking about when you have had experiences in these zones. In each of the boxes below, draw or write about a time when you were in that zone.

Red Zone (Overresponding)

Yellow Zone (Underresponding)

Green Zone (You are good to go!)

Learning About Feelings

During EMDR therapy, it will be important for us to learn more about your emotions and how you express them. Everyone has feelings that are easy to share and also feelings that are harder to talk about. One of our goals in EMDR therapy during phase 2 is to help you learn how to identify and share your feelings in a healthy manner.

Directions:

■ Color in the square completely if the feeling is easy for you to share and express.

◩ Color in the square halfway if the feeling is a little hard to talk about sometimes.

☐ Leave the square blank if the feeling is very hard to talk about and share.

You can come back to this page at any time and color in the squares completely when you are ready!

☐ Happy   ☐ Calm

☐ Mad   ☐ Lonely

☐ Worried   ☐ Loved

☐ Afraid   ☐ Sad

☐ Disgusted   ☐ Guilty

☐ Surprised   ☐ Embarrassed

☐ Ashamed   ☐ Silly

☐ Joyful   ☐ Confused

☐ Excited   ☐ Curious

☐ Jealous   ☐ Safe

☐ Shy   ☐ Proud

☐ Brave   ☐ Disappointed

Coping and Calming Skills Checklist

Did you know that you probably already have a bunch of skills to help you stay calm and cope when things get hard? Below is a list of common coping and calming skills for kids. Put a star by the skills you already do. Put a check mark by any skills you would like to learn or try. In the blank spaces, write in other skills you do or want to try to help you feel calmer.

☐ Listen to music

☐ Play with toys

☐ Drink water

☐ Eat a snack

☐ Talk to a trusted adult

☐ Talk to a friend

☐ Play with pets

☐ Read

☐ Draw or color

☐ Do yoga

☐ Journal or write

☐ Go for a walk, jog, or hike

☐ Ask for help

☐ _____

☐ _____

☐ _____

☐ Sing

☐ Do arts and crafts

☐ Take a bath or shower

☐ Think of a happy place

☐ Do deep breathing

☐ Play a game

☐ Make slime

☐ Say positive thoughts

☐ Play outside

☐ Exercise

☐ Dance

☐ Blow bubbles

☐ Take a break

☐ _____

☐ _____

☐ _____

Happy Place

Imagine a place where you feel happy. This place can be real or imagined. For example, it could be a place you have gone on vacation or a magical castle in the clouds. Use all five senses (sight, sound, smell, taste, and touch) to describe your happy place. Optional: With your EMDR therapist, use back-and-forth movement to strengthen your happy place.

Draw your happy place!

Safe, Calm Place

Imagine a place where you feel safe and calm. This place can be real or imagined. For example, it could be a cozy corner of your house or a magical place from your imagination. Use all five senses (sight, sound, smell, taste, and touch) to describe your safe, calm place. Optional: With your EMDR therapist, use back-and-forth movement to strengthen your safe, calm place.

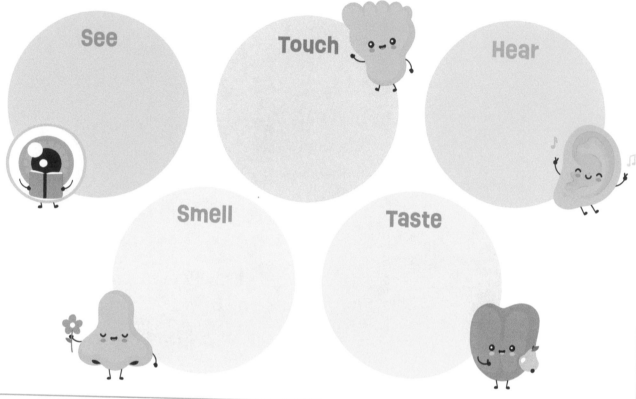

See

Touch

Hear

Smell

Taste

Draw your safe, calm place!

Light Stream

Think about your target problem and notice how it feels in your body. Draw the shape, size, and color of the problem in body 1. For body 2, pick a color for healing, and color in all the areas of your body that need this healing color. As you are coloring, take deep breaths and imagine that you are breathing in a color of healing. As you breathe out, imagine the color of the problem leaving your body.

Container Exercise

When feelings and memories get too overwhelming and take over your brain, imagine putting it all in a container for safekeeping. This container will hold all these feelings and memories until you are ready to come back to them later. You can create your own container or use the mason jar below. Write or draw all of the feelings and memories that need to be contained in this jar. If you decide to create your own jar, don't forget to also place a lid on your container!

Breathing Shift

1. Bring up a happy or positive memory.

2. Notice where you feel your breath in your body.

3. Put your hand on this part of your body. Take two to three deep breaths.

4. Now bring up a memory that is just a little bit stressful.

5. Notice if your breathing changes. Put your hand over where you feel your breath now.

6. Next, put your hand in the first location, and change your breathing back to how it felt when you were thinking about something happy or positive. Take two to three deep breaths.

Breathe and move your where it feels good

Breathe and move your where you feel stress

Breathe and move your where it feels good

Unhelpful and Helpful Thoughts

Circle the unhelpful thoughts that bother you the most when you think about the target problem you are having. Draw a cloud around the helpful thoughts you would like to have instead.

Unhelpful Thoughts

I AM BAD

I'M NOT IN CONTROL

I AM NOT LOVABLE

I'M NOT GOOD ENOUGH

I CAN NEVER GET IT RIGHT

I CAN'T HANDLE IT

I CAN'T DO IT

I DON'T BELONG

I DON'T UNDERSTAND

I'M NOT SAFE

I AM UGLY

I CAN'T PROTECT MYSELF

I CAN'T TRUST ANYONE

I CAN'T ASK FOR HELP

I MESSED UP

I AM EXPLODING

I CAN'T LEARN

I CAN'T FIGURE IT OUT

I AM STUPID

I DON'T KNOW HOW

I'M LOST

I AM THE WORST

I NEED TO BE PERFECT

I AM MEAN

Helpful Thoughts

I AM GOOD

I AM IN CONTROL

I AM LOVABLE

I AM ENOUGH

I CAN FIGURE THINGS OUT

I CAN HANDLE IT

I CAN TRY MY BEST

I DO BELONG

I DO UNDERSTAND

I AM SAFE

I AM FINE JUST THE WAY I AM

I CAN PROTECT MYSELF

I CAN CHOOSE WHOM TO TRUST

I CAN ASK FOR HELP

I DID MY BEST

I CAN STAY CALM

I CAN LEARN

I CAN FIGURE IT OUT

I AM LEARNING

I CAN LEARN HOW

I CAN FIND MY WAY

I DID MY BEST

I CAN MAKE MISTAKES

I AM KIND

Adapted from Shapiro (2018) and Adler-Tapia & Settle (2008)

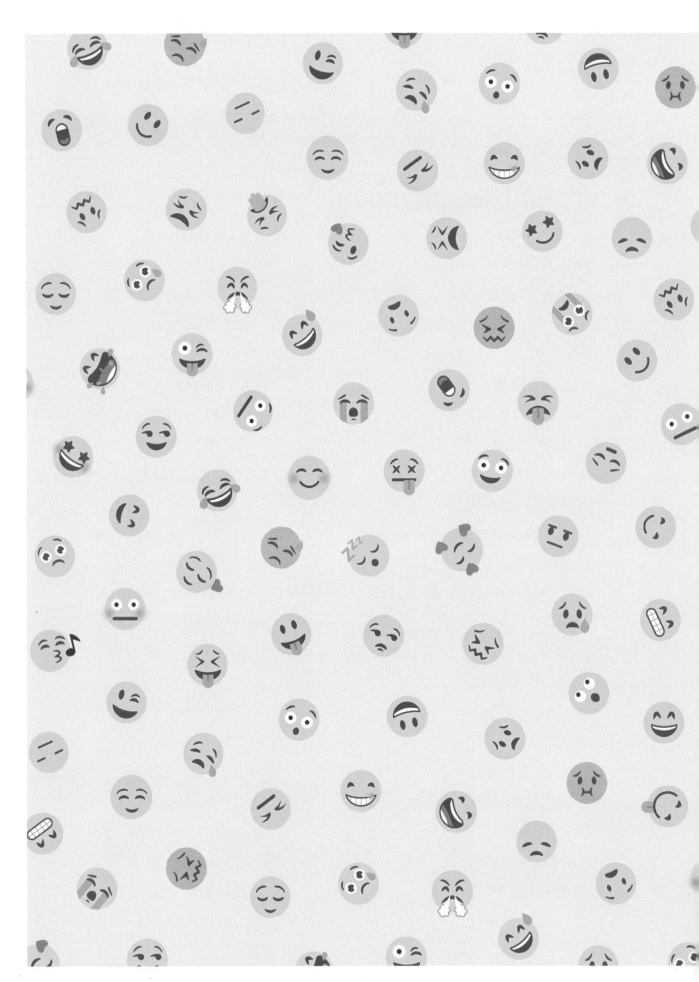

Unhelpful Thought Cards

Cut out the following unhelpful thoughts to create a card deck. You can use this deck when doing EMDR therapy to help you figure out what thought matches the problem you are having.

I AM BAD	I CAN'T LEARN	I AM THE WORST
I'M NOT IN CONTROL	I MESSED UP	I AM EXPLODING
I AM NOT LOVABLE	I AM UGLY	I CAN'T ASK FOR HELP
I AM NOT GOOD ENOUGH	I DON'T UNDERSTAND	I'M NOT SAFE
I'M STUPID	I CAN'T PROTECT MYSELF	I CAN'T TRUST ANYONE
I CAN'T HANDLE IT	I CAN'T DO IT	I DON'T BELONG

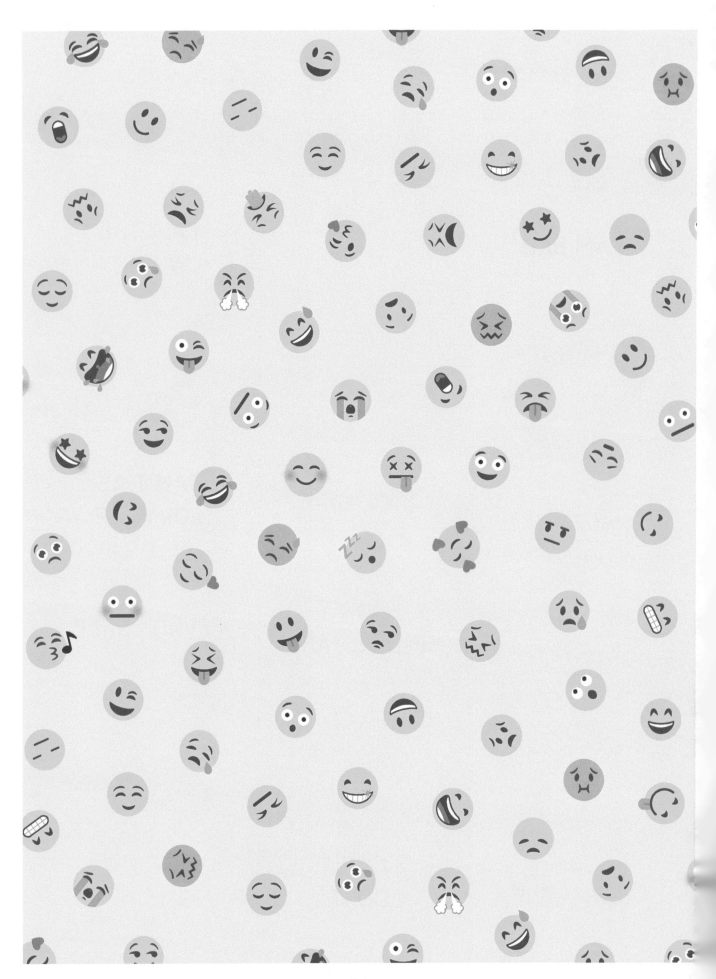

I CAN'T FIGURE IT OUT	I DON'T KNOW HOW	I'M LOST
I NEED TO BE PERFECT	I CAN NEVER GET IT RIGHT	I AM MEAN

CREATE YOUR OWN	CREATE YOUR OWN	CREATE YOUR OWN
CREATE YOUR OWN	CREATE YOUR OWN	CREATE YOUR OWN
CREATE YOUR OWN	CREATE YOUR OWN	CREATE YOUR OWN
CREATE YOUR OWN	CREATE YOUR OWN	CREATE YOUR OWN
CREATE YOUR OWN	CREATE YOUR OWN	CREATE YOUR OWN

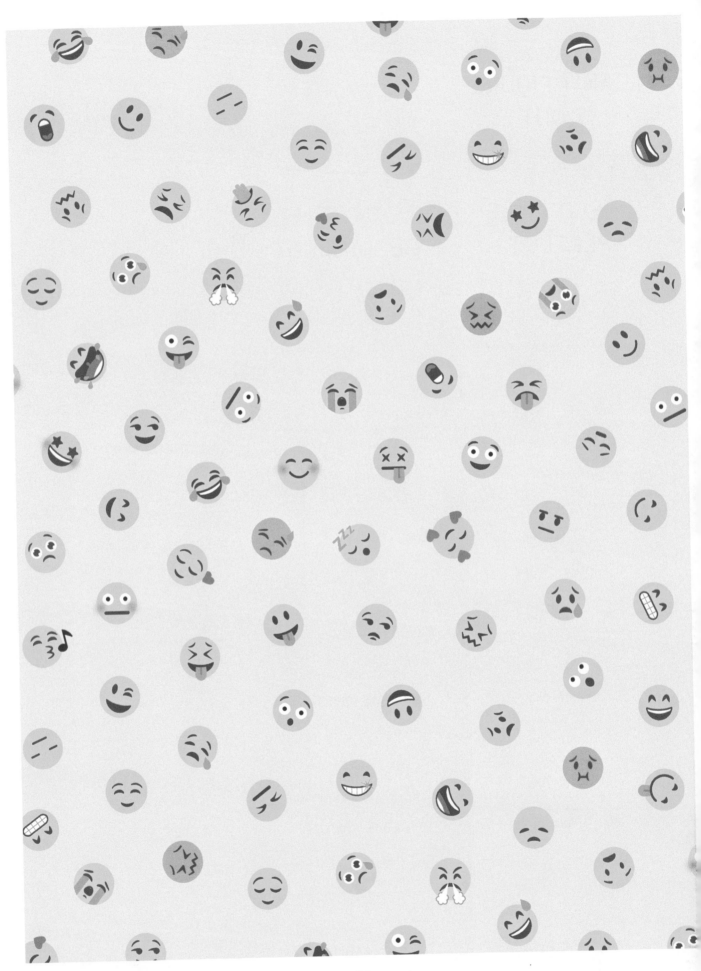

Helpful Thought Cards

Cut out the following helpful thoughts to create a card deck. You can use this deck when doing EMDR therapy to help you figure out the thought you would like to have for your problems instead.

I AM GOOD	I CAN LEARN	I DID MY BEST
I AM IN CONTROL	I CAN MAKE MISTAKES	I CAN STAY CALM
I AM LOVABLE	I AM FINE JUST THE WAY I AM	I CAN ASK FOR HELP
I AM ENOUGH	I DO UNDERSTAND	I AM SAFE
I AM LEARNING	I CAN PROTECT MYSELF	I CAN CHOOSE WHOM TO TRUST
I CAN HANDLE IT	I CAN TRY MY BEST	I DO BELONG

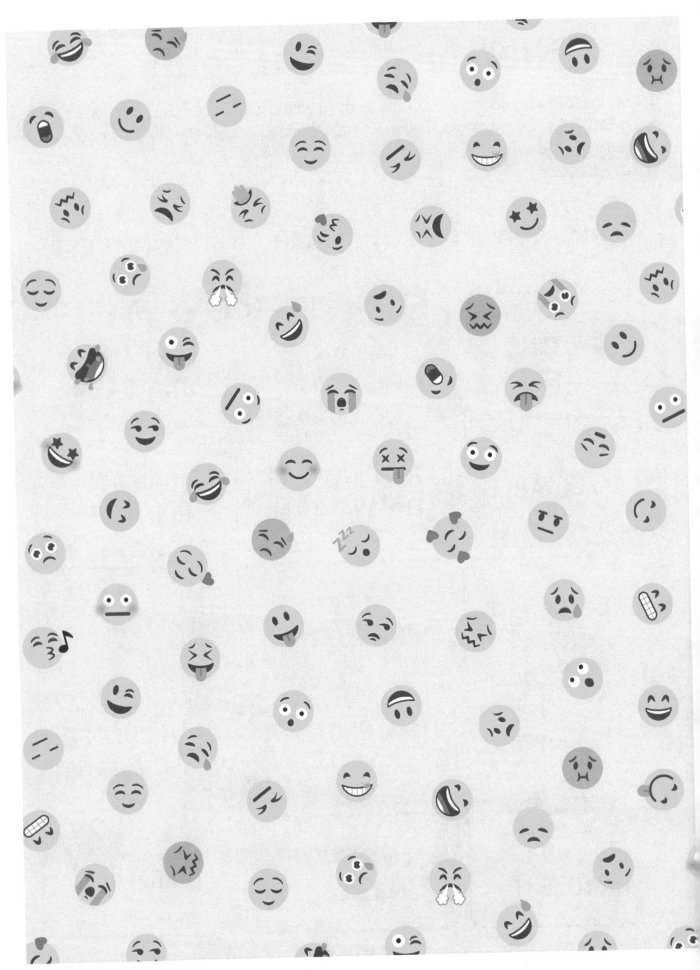

I CAN FIGURE IT OUT	I CAN LEARN HOW	I CAN FIND MY WAY
I CAN MAKE MISTAKES	I CAN FIGURE THINGS OUT	I AM KIND
CREATE YOUR OWN	CREATE YOUR OWN	CREATE YOUR OWN
CREATE YOUR OWN	CREATE YOUR OWN	CREATE YOUR OWN
CREATE YOUR OWN	CREATE YOUR OWN	CREATE YOUR OWN
CREATE YOUR OWN	CREATE YOUR OWN	CREATE YOUR OWN
CREATE YOUR OWN	CREATE YOUR OWN	CREATE YOUR OWN

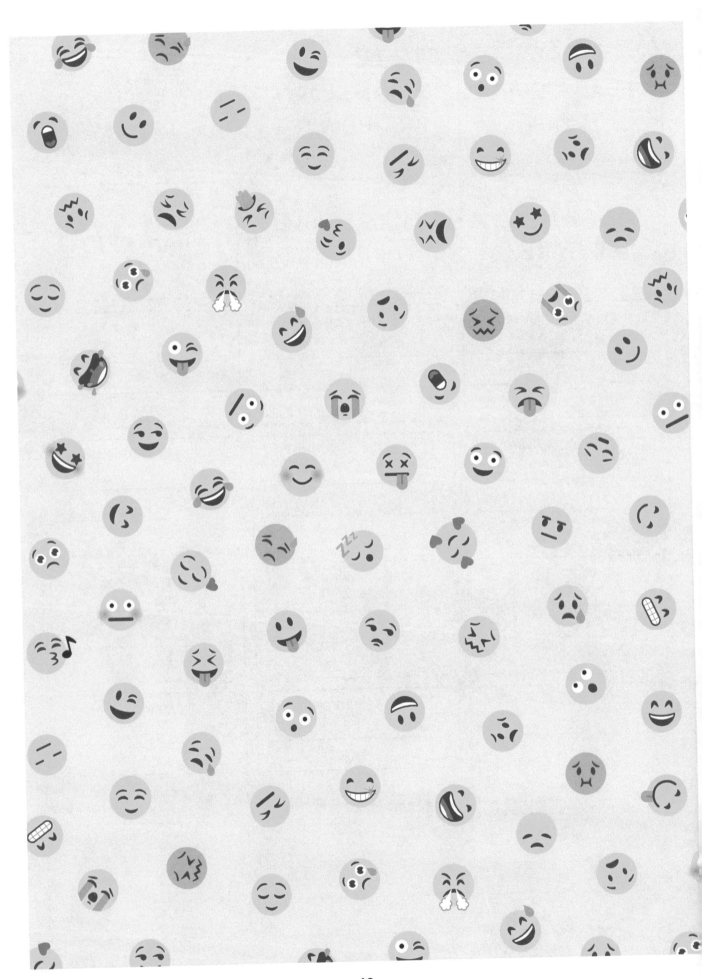

Resource Development and Installation Instructions

The purpose of resource development and installation (RDI) is to help you develop and strengthen specific qualities and abilities. Common qualities that many kids like to strengthen include feeling strong, being flexible, being patient, or feeling brave. You may have felt these qualities when riding your bike, playing music, making art, helping a friend, or playing sports.

Instructions

There are three kinds of resources:

1. **Mastery resources** are times when you have done something well.
2. **Relational resources** are times when you saw someone else do something well. This might be a person in your life or a character in a movie, cartoon, or story.
3. **Symbolic resources** are images or symbols that represent good things to you, like animals, plants, or other elements of the earth (like wind or fire). For example, maybe you picture a tiger as strong or a tree as flexible.

1. What qualities or abilities would help you as you think about the scary, confusing, or traumatic event? Select a quality or ability that you would like to make stronger for yourself so you can handle this event. Write or draw this in box 1 on the RDI worksheet.

2. Describe a time when you, someone else, or something else had this quality. Write or draw this in box 2.

3. Identify an image that makes you think of this quality. For example, if you want to feel braver, maybe the image of a superhero best represents the resource of bravery. Write or draw this in box 3.

4. As you think about the quality, what do you see, hear, and feel right now? What do you notice? Write or draw this in box 4.
   Your EMDR therapist will guide you through 4 to 12 slow back-and-forth movements of your choice to strengthen this resource.

Adapted from Shapiro (2018), Korn & Leeds (2002), and Adler-Tapia & Settle (2008)

5. Is there a word or phrase that represents this quality? Think of this cue word and notice the positive feelings you have when you think of that word. Concentrate on those feelings and the cue word while doing back-and-forth movements. Write your cue word in box 5.

   Your EMDR therapist will guide you through 4 to 12 slow back-and-forth movements of your choice to strengthen your resource with your chosen cue word.

6. Play a movie in your mind where you imagine using this quality. Imagine you are watching a YouTube video of yourself where you are able to deal with a challenging situation by using your new resource! What do you notice? Write or draw this in box 6.

   Your EMDR therapist will guide you through 4 to 12 slow back-and-forth movements of your choice to strengthen your resource.

7. Optional: Play another video in your mind where you are responding to another challenging situation with your selected quality. What do you notice? Write or draw this in box 7.

   Your EMDR therapist will guide you through 4 to 12 slow back-and-forth movements of your choice.

8. Draw a picture of yourself handling your problems well with your new or strengthened quality in box 8.

Adapted from Shapiro (2018), Korn & Leeds (2002), and Adler-Tapia & Settle (2008)

Resource Development and Installation Worksheet

Mastery	**Relational**	**Symbolic**
Your own experiences when you did something well	Role models or characters who have done something well	Animal or element that symbolizes good things to you

1. What quality or ability is needed?

2. When is a time that you, or someone or something else, had this quality?

3. What image do you picture for this quality?

4. What do you see, hear, and feel right now when you think of the quality?

5. Write your cue word(s) for this quality.

6. Play a movie where you use the quality to overcome a challenging situation.

7. Play another movie (optional).

8. Draw a picture of yourself handling your problems well with your new quality.

Adapted from Shapiro (2018), Korn & Leeds (2002), and Adler-Tapia & Settle (2008)

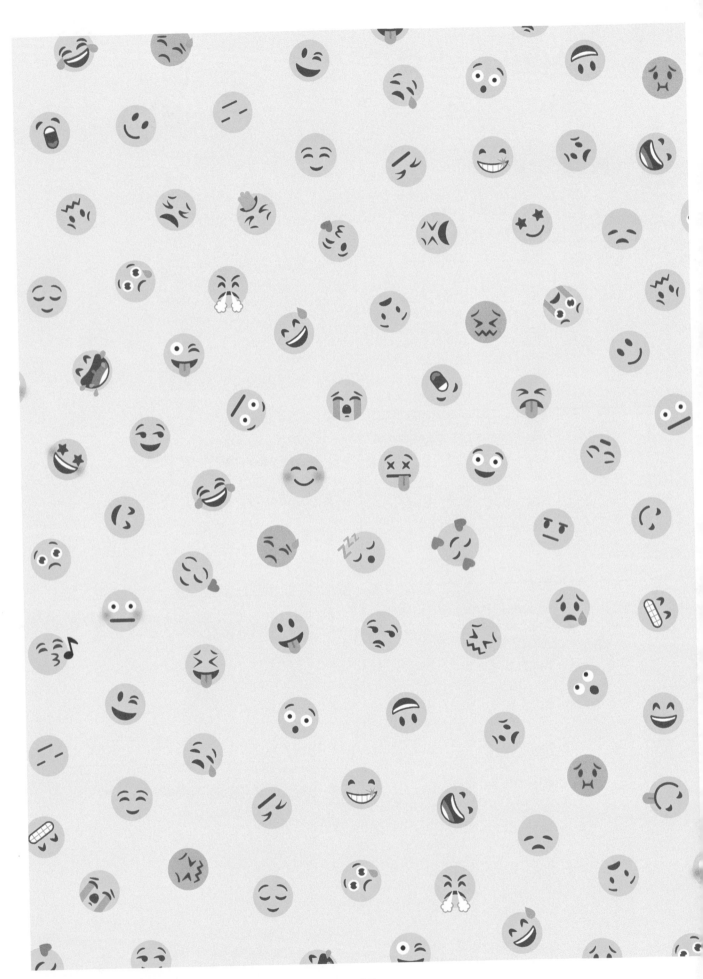

CHAPTER 3

PHASE 3: Activating Targets

Phase 3 of EMDR is what Francine Shapiro calls the "assessment" phase. We will work together to gather information and get you ready to begin phase 4 of treatment. According to Francine Shapiro (2018), you need to do the following things in phase 3 so you will be ready for phase 4:

1. Select a specific target problem, memory, event, or symptom you want to work on.

2. Select an image or picture that comes to your mind when you think about this problem.

3. Identify a negative or unhelpful thought you have about the problem.

4. Identify a positive or helpful thought you would like to have instead.

5. Rate how true the positive thought feels on a scale of 1 to 7 (with 1 being "not true at all" and 7 being "completely true").

6. Identify the emotions you feel when you think about this problem.

7. Rate how stressful this problem feels on a scale of 0 to 10 (where 0 means "not stressed at all" and 10 is "the most stress you could feel").

8. Identify the body sensations you feel when you think about this problem.

The following worksheets will help you and your therapist complete these steps.

Clinician Tip: Choose SUD and VOC scales that will be the most developmentally appropriate for each child. Some scales are aligned with Francine Shapiro's 10-point SUD scale and 7-point VOC scale, while other scales are simplified for young children (e.g., only giving three choices of small, medium, or big).

EMDR Standard Protocol Instructions

This worksheet will help you gather all the information you need for phase 3 of EMDR.

Instructions

Use the worksheet that follows to complete these steps:

1. Select a specific target problem, memory, event, or symptom.

2. Select an image or picture that best represents the target problem.

3. Identify a negative or unhelpful thought (negative cognition) associated with the target problem.

4. Identify a positive or helpful thought (positive cognition) that you'd like to have about the target problem instead.

5. Rate the validity of cognition (VOC) by asking yourself: How true does the helpful thought feel on a scale of 1 to 7 (where 1 = "not true at all" and 7 = "completely true")?

6. Identify the emotions you feel when you think about the target problem.

7. Rate your subjective unit of disturbance (SUD) by asking yourself: How stressed out does the problem make you feel on a scale of 0 to 10 (where 0 = "no stress at all" and 10 = "the most stress you could ever feel")?

8. Identify the body sensations you feel when you think about the target problem. Color or draw what you feel in your body.

Reference: Shapiro (2018)

EMDR Standard Protocol Worksheet

 1. Target problem

 2. Target picture

 3. Unhelpful thought

 4. Helpful thought

VOC
5. How true is your helpful thought?

① ② ③ ④ ⑤ ⑥ ⑦

6. What feelings do you feel?

Happy   Sad   Mad   Worried

Scared   Hurt   Confused   Draw your own

SUD
7. How stressed does the problem make you feel?

8. What do you feel in your body?

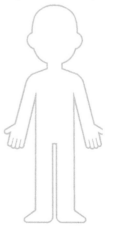

Reference: Shapiro (2018)

SUD Scale

How stressed do you feel when you think about the problem on a scale of 0 to 10?

10 The most stress ever

9

8 Huge level of stress

7 Big level of stress

6

5 Medium level of stress

4

3 A little bit of stress

2 A tiny bit of stress

1

0 No stress at all

Reference: Shapiro (2018)

VOC Scale

How true is your helpful thought on a scale of 1 to 7?

 Not true at all

 A little true

Somewhat true

Very true

Completely true

Reference: Shapiro (2018)

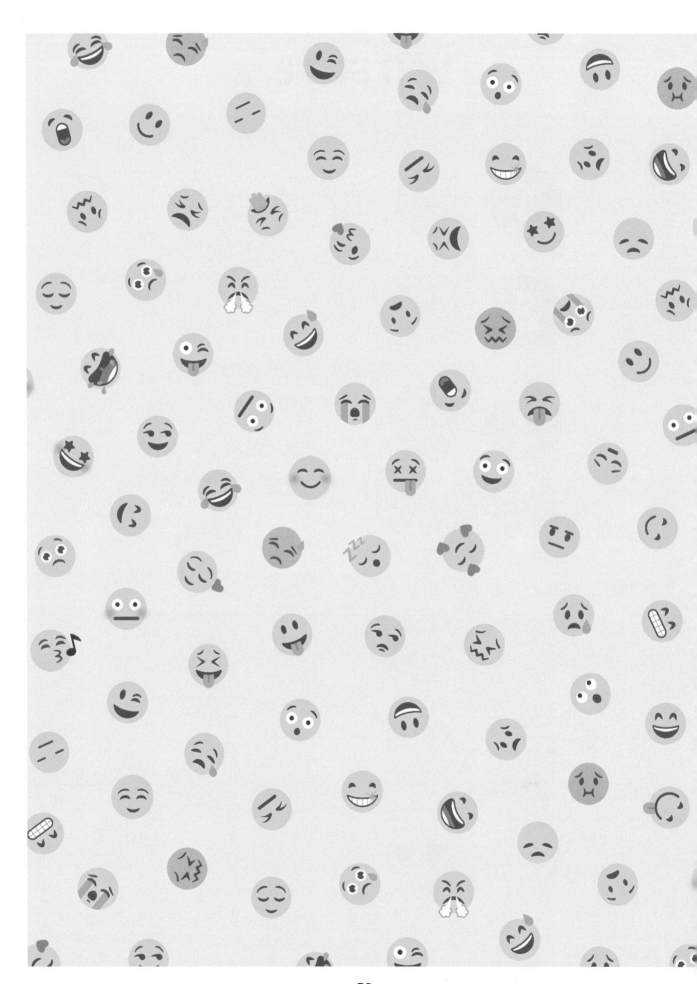

Dump Truck SUD Scale

Sometimes, our problems can feel like they are as big as a dump truck! To determine how big your problem feels right now, cut out the dump truck and each pile of rocks. Then rate how big your problem feels by adding piles of rocks to your dump truck that match your stress level (where 0 piles of rocks = "no stress at all" and 10 piles of rocks = "the most stress you could ever feel").

Dump Truck VOC Scale

To determine how true your helpful thought feels right now, cut out the dump truck and the VOC scale. Then place the dump truck on the number that shows how true the thought feels.

VOC Scale

1 Not true at all

2

A little true

3

4 Somewhat true

5

Very true

6

7 Completely true

Waves SUD Scale

Sometimes, our problems can feel like big waves crashing onto us. How big of a wave does your problem feel like right now?

10
9
8

A huge wave

7
6

A very big wave

5
4

A big wave

3
2

A small wave

1
0

No waves, just calm water

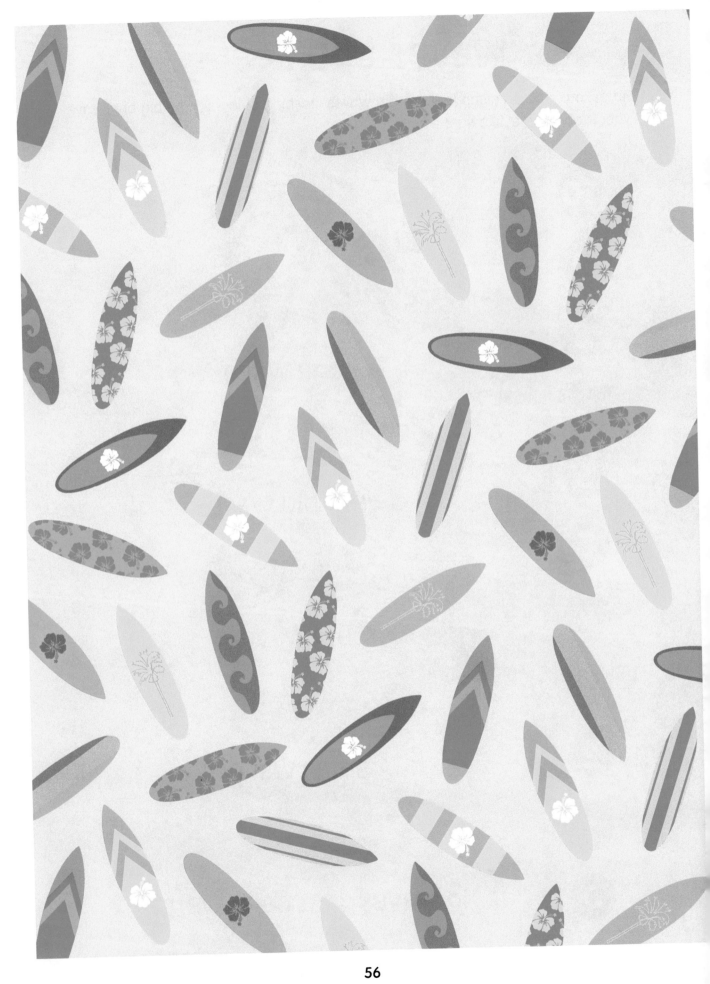

Waves VOC Scale

To determine how true your helpful thought feels right now, cut out your favorite surfboard and the VOC scale. Then place your surfboard on the wave that shows how true the thought feels.

VOC Scale

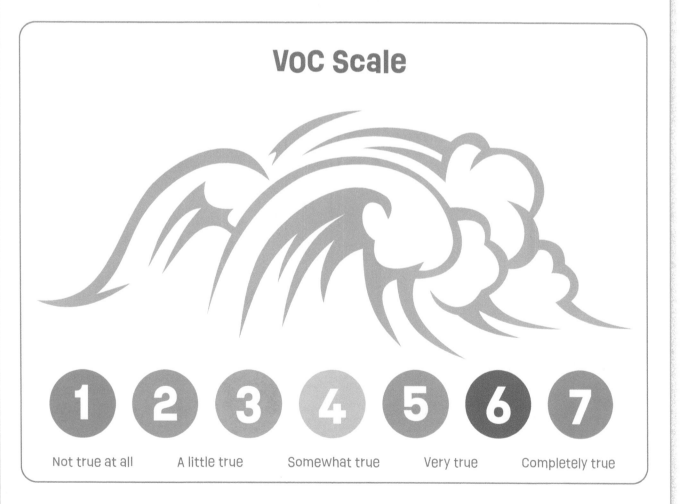

1	2	3	4	5	6	7
Not true at all		A little true		Somewhat true		Very true	Completely true

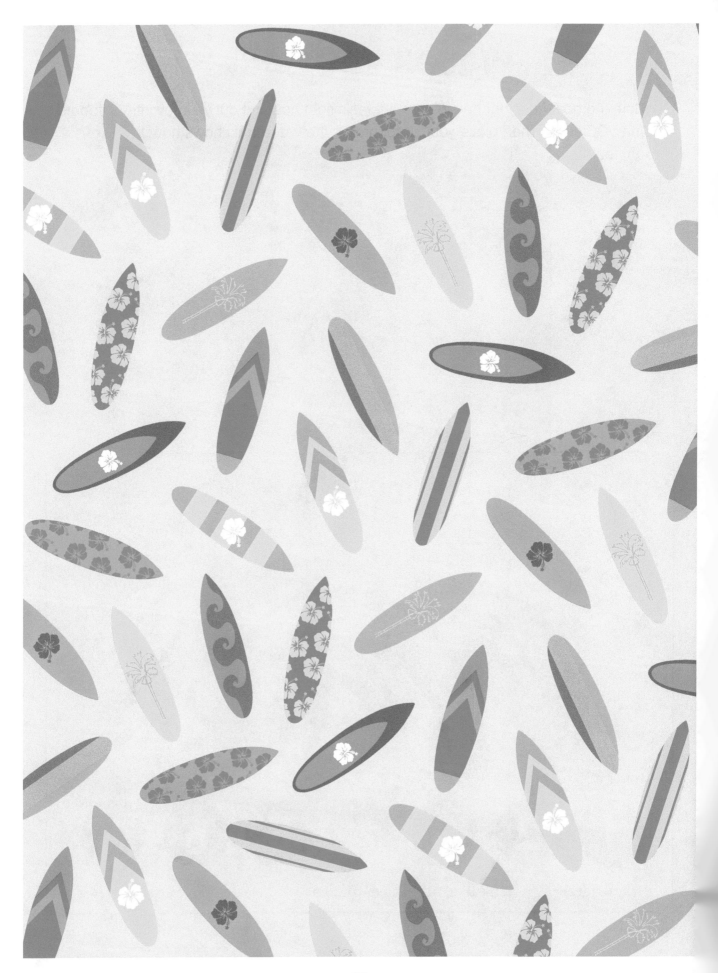

Whale SUD Scale

Sometimes our problems can feel as big as a whale! How big does your problem feel when you think about it now? Small, medium, or big?

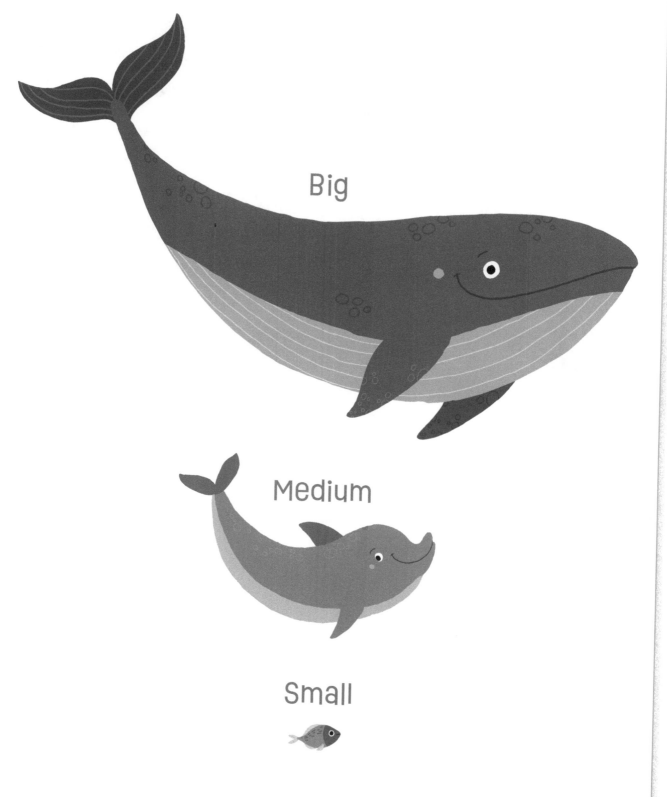

Big

Medium

Small

Whale VOC Scale

To determine how true your helpful thought feels right now, cut out the whale and the VOC scale. Then place the whale on the number that shows how true the thought feels.

VOC Scale

1 Not true at all

2 A little true

3

4 Somewhat true

5 Very true

6

7 Completely true

Stormy SUD Scale

Sometimes our problems can feel like a big thunderstorm raining down on us. How stormy does your problem feel when you think about it now?

10 9 The biggest storm you could imagine, with thunder and lightning!

8

7 A hard storm

6

5 A rainstorm

4

3

2 A little rain shower

1

0 Not stormy at all

Rainbow VOC Scale

To determine how true your helpful thought feels right now, color in the rainbow below. One color means that your helpful thought does not feel true at all, while seven colors means it feels completely true.

 Helpful thought

How many colors of the rainbow does your helpful thought feel?

7 colors = Completely true

6 colors = Very true

5 colors = Mostly true

4 colors = Pretty true

3 colors = Somewhat true

2 colors = A little true

1 color = Not true at all

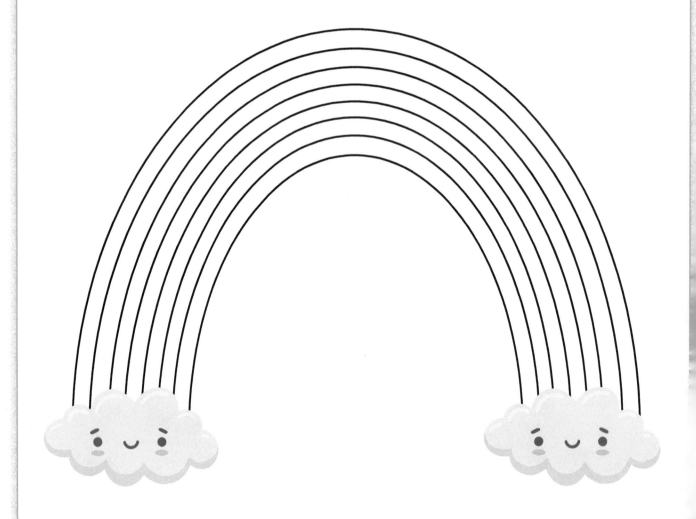

Pizza SUD Scale

Sometimes our problems can feel overwhelming, like an extra-large pizza. How big does your problem feel when you think about it now? Mini, medium, large, or extra-large?

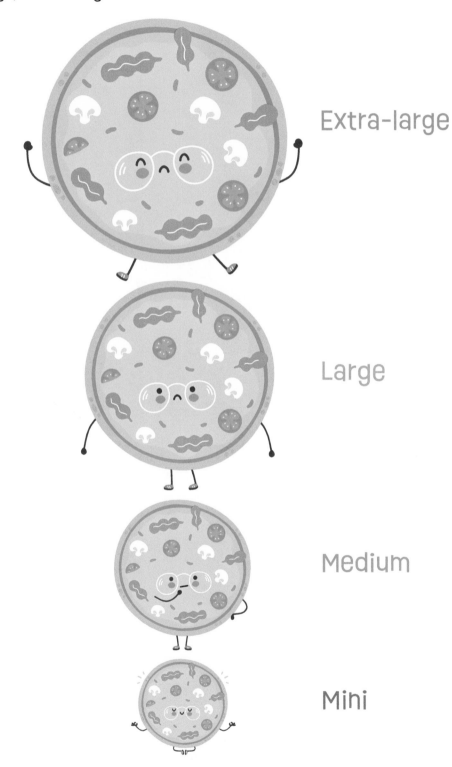

Extra-large

Large

Medium

Mini

Pizza VOC Scale

To determine how true your helpful thought feels right now, color in the slices of this pizza pie. One slice means that your helpful thought does not feel true at all, while seven slices means it feels completely true. You may also color and cut out the slices to create a pizza VOC scale that you can use during EMDR therapy.

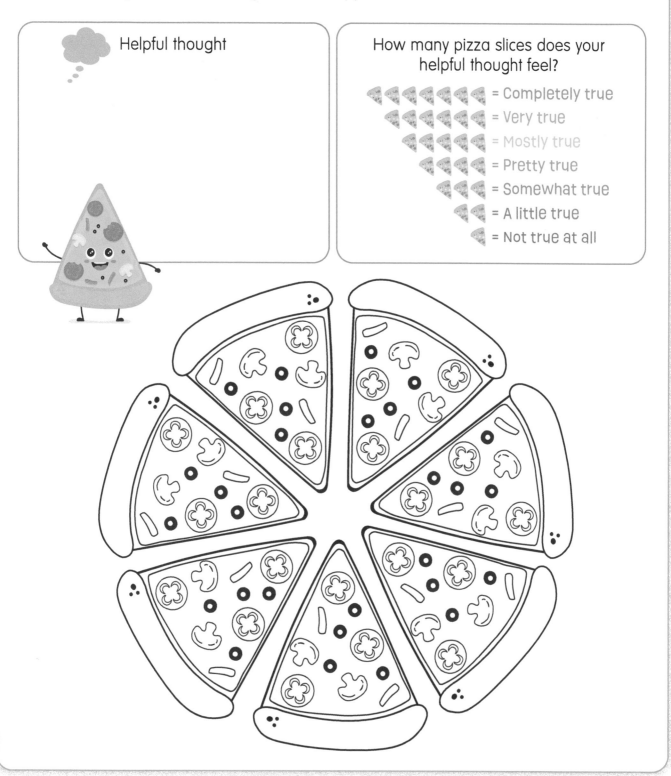

Helpful thought

How many pizza slices does your helpful thought feel?

= Completely true
= Very true
= Mostly true
= Pretty true
= Somewhat true
= A little true
= Not true at all

CHAPTER 4

PHASE 4: Discharging the Stress

During phase 4 of EMDR therapy, you will focus on getting rid of the stress that is stuck in your mind, heart, and body as a result of the traumatic or scary event you experienced. Francine Shapiro calls this phase "desensitization," which is a fancy word to explain how EMDR helps you feel less sensitive to scary things that happened to you in the past. And when you feel less sensitive to these things, that means they don't bother you as much anymore!

During phase 4, your therapist will ask you to do two things at once: The first thing you will do is focus on the problem you have chosen to work on. The second thing you will do is bilateral stimulation, which refers to those back-and-forth movements we talked about earlier. Have you ever done two things at the same time? Use the following worksheet to practice doing two things at once!

Clinician Tip: Be prepared to help children engage in a variety of bilateral stimulation or back-and-forth movements. Some children may be perfectly content using the same type of back-and-forth movement for the entire EMDR session, while others may want to use many types of movement in one session. For virtual therapy sessions with children, therapists can use online tools such as Bilateralstimulation.io, which offers child-friendly images, such as dragons and emojis, to help engage children online.

Doing Two Things

Let's have some fun practicing doing two things at once before we explore how this is helpful in EMDR therapy. Try doing the following things at the same time. Create your own challenge with your therapist too!

 Stand on one leg and count to 10.

 Stand on your tip toes and reach your hands to the sky!

 Color and hum your favorite song.

 Pat your head and rub your tummy!

 Wiggle your toes and whistle.

 Blink your eyes and spell your name.

 Watch a video and eat a snack.

 Listen to music and dance.

 Bounce a ball and say your ABCs.

 Make a silly face and a silly sound.

Create your own two things to do at the same time!

Create your own two things to do at the same time!

Bilateral Stimulation

As you focus on the problem and do back-and-forth movements, your brain work will hard to remove all the roadblocks that this problem is causing for you. Your brain will also work hard to rebuild the roads in your brain so this problem stops bothering you so much. The goal in phase 4 is to help you feel no stress or very little stress when you think about the traumatic memory now or are reminded of it in the future.

The back-and-forth movements have an important goal: They help move the negative thoughts, feelings, and body sensations you have about a problem in a more positive direction. For example, let's say you have a problem that makes you think "I'm a bad kid," which leads you to feel sad and gives you a funny feeling in your stomach and heart. The back-and-forth movements will help to rebuild the roads in your brain so you can have a healthier thought about the same problem, like "I'm a good kid, and I made a mistake." When you have positive and helpful thoughts about the problem, you will feel much happier, and your body will feel much better.

The following worksheets will give you some more ideas for types of back-and-forth movements that you can do during phase 4. It is important for you to pick movements that work best for *you* so you can remove the roadblocks that are keeping you stuck and move your thoughts, feelings, and body sensations in a more positive direction.

Moving My Eyes

Moving your eyes back and forth is the first thing that Francine Shapiro discovered could help many people in EMDR therapy. Use the steps below to practice moving your eyes with your EMDR therapist.

Step 1

Find a comfortable place to sit.

Step 2

Without moving your head, move only your eyes back and forth. Your EMDR therapist can guide you to follow their fingers, finger puppets, balls, or toys.

Step 3

With your EMDR therapist, you can practice moving your eyes in different directions (e.g., back and forth, diagonal, up and down, in a figure 8).

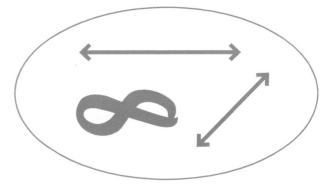

Step 4

With your EMDR therapist, you can also practice moving your eyes at different speeds. Practice moving your eyes as fast as you can! Then practice moving your eyes as slowly as you can.

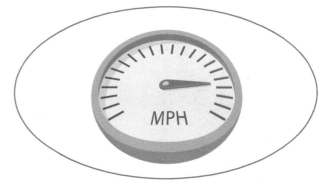

Reference: Shapiro (2018)

Butterfly Hug

The butterfly hug was created by Lucina (Lucy) Artigas and her husband, Ignacio (Nacho) Jarero, to help people who had experienced a hurricane. This exercise is used by many people to help them feel better. Follow the steps below to learn the butterfly hug!

Step 1

With your palms facing up, cross your thumbs to create a butterfly shape. Gently flutter your butterfly wings!

Step 2

Place your butterfly over your heart!

Step 3

Make sure your butterfly wings (fingertips) are touching your collarbones.

Step 4

Slowly tap your butterfly wings (fingertips) one at a time on your collarbone 8 to 10 times. Right, left, right, left, right, left...

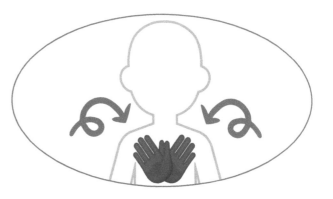

Reference: Artigas et al. (2000)

Gorilla Taps

In this type of back-and-forth movement, you get to pretend that you are a gorilla! Follow the steps below to learn the gorilla tap.

Step 1

Make a fist with both your hands and cross your wrists.

Step 2

Bring your arms and hands over your chest and heart.

Step 3

Make sure your fists are slightly under your collarbones.

Step 4

Slowly tap your gorilla hands (fists) one at a time on your collarbone 8 to 10 times. Right, left, right, left, right, left...

Reference: Artigas et al. (2000)

Games and Activities For Bilateral Stimulation

There are lots of games and activities that can be used to complete the back-and-forth movements needed during phase 4 of EMDR therapy. Try out the games and activities below to see which ones will work for you!

EMDR Simon Says

Take turns with your EMDR therapist playing "EMDR Simon Says." For example, "EMDR Simon says run in place for 20 seconds."

EMDR Hopscotch

Create a hopscotch game to hop and jump for bilateral stimulation! You can use tape indoors or go outside and use sidewalk chalk.

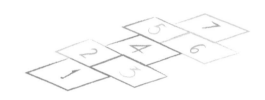

EMDR Head, Shoulders, Knees, and Toes

Tap on your head, shoulders, knees, and toes—tapping back and forth on each part of your body about 10 times. Make it fun by singing the song or adding music.

EMDR Jump Rope

You can use the jump rope to jump side to side or challenge yourself to jump on one foot and then the other.

EMDR Dance

Create a dance where you go back and forth or side to side with your therapist. Make it fun by playing your favorite music!

Make Your Own EMDR Activity

Can you think of other games or activities you can do during EMDR therapy to create back-and-forth movement? Brainstorm with your EMDR therapist!

CHAPTER 5

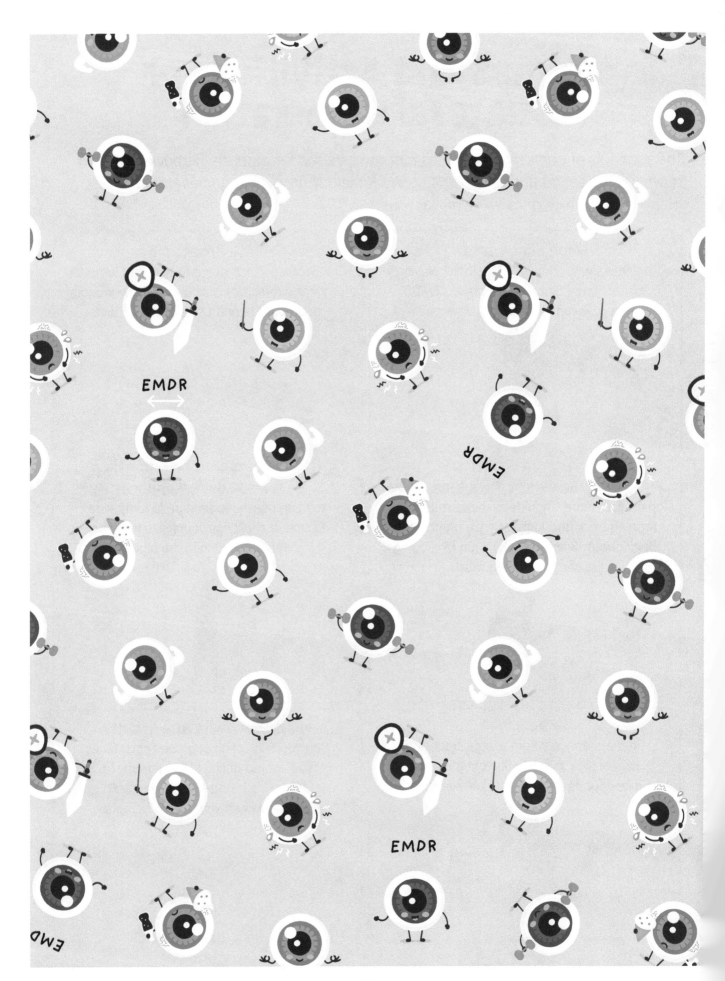

PHASE 5:
Strengthening the Positive

Phase 5 of EMDR therapy is focused on strengthening the positive thoughts you have about yourself. That means you're going to work on helping these thoughts feel truer. Francine Shapiro calls this phase "installation."

When bad things have repeatedly happened to us, it can be hard to believe positive things about ourselves. Sometimes, we know that something positive about us is true, but it doesn't *feel* true. For example, a kid might know that they are smart after getting a good grade on their spelling test, but they might still *feel* dumb.

You have already done most of the hard work in phase 4 by using back-and-forth movements to shift your negative thoughts, feelings, and body sensations in a more positive direction. Once you are in phase 5, most of that negative stuff will already have been unblocked from your brain!

In phase 5, you will continue using back-and-forth movements with your EMDR therapist to help your positive thoughts feel truer. You are basically working to change your self-talk, which is a fancy word for how you talk about yourself. The following worksheets will help you remember previous times when you had positive self-talk and help you reflect on your self-talk before and after an EMDR session.

> **Clinician Tip:** Offer a variety of playful ways in which the child can strengthen their positive thoughts during this phase. For example, the child could say their positive thought into a microphone toy or say it to themselves while looking in a mirror!

My Positive Thoughts and Memories

In the left-hand column, write down positive thoughts you would like to have about yourself when you think about the target problems you have been working on in EMDR therapy. In the right-hand column, write down memories of times when you previously had these positive thoughts about yourself. For example, maybe you want to have the positive thought "I am brave" and remember a time when you were brave at a doctor's appointment.

Positive Thoughts About Me

Memories of Me

Before and After Self-Talk

Let's take a look at your thoughts before and after an EMDR session. Write an unhelpful thought you had about a problem before starting EMDR therapy and draw what that looks like on the left-hand side of the page. After the EMDR therapy session, write and draw what helpful thought you believe instead on the right-hand side of the page.

Unhelpful Thought

Helpful Thought

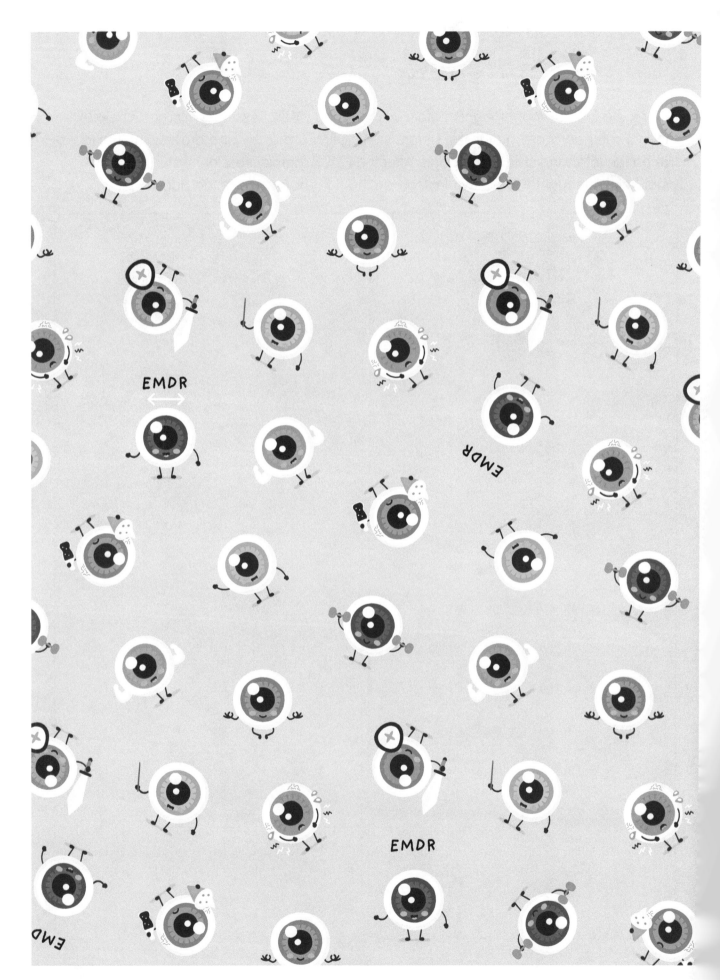

CHAPTER 6

PHASE 6:
Increasing Body Awareness

Did you know that your body has memory too? You might have heard people talk about "muscle memory." Without thinking too much about it, your body just knows how to walk, jump, or even ride a bike. These are all good memories for your body to have so you can run, dance, and play.

But it can become a problem when your body has negative or unhelpful memories stuck in it. For example, let's say your body is stuck in a memory of a time when you broke your arm. Even though the accident is over and your arm is healed, you still feel pain and weakness in that arm. Maybe this pain and weakness begins to hold you back from trying new things at the playground or learning how to cartwheel. When this happens, your body stays stuck when it doesn't need to be!

The goal of phase 6 is to help you get rid of any body memories that aren't helpful for you anymore. Francine Shapiro calls this phase the "body scan." With your EMDR therapist, you will figure out what sensations are still stuck in your body when you think about the traumatic or scary event that happened to you in the past. You will work on getting those memories unstuck so your body feels much better.

The following worksheets will help you learn more about your body sensations and process the sensations that may be stuck.

Clinician Tip: Make this phase playful and fun by offering the use of puppets, stuffed animals, or toys to help complete the body scan. For example, if a child picks a teddy bear to help them, you might give the bear the following instructions: "Hello, Mr. Bear! [Child's name] is working on getting rid of uncomfortable feelings in their body when they think about [target problem]. Can you help us scan [child's name] body and let us know if there are any uncomfortable body feelings anywhere?"

My Body Sensations

Different types of feelings can give us different types of body sensations. For each feeling below, draw or color in how your body feels when you experience that emotion.

Happy   Sad   Mad   Confused

Worried   Excited   Scared   Loved

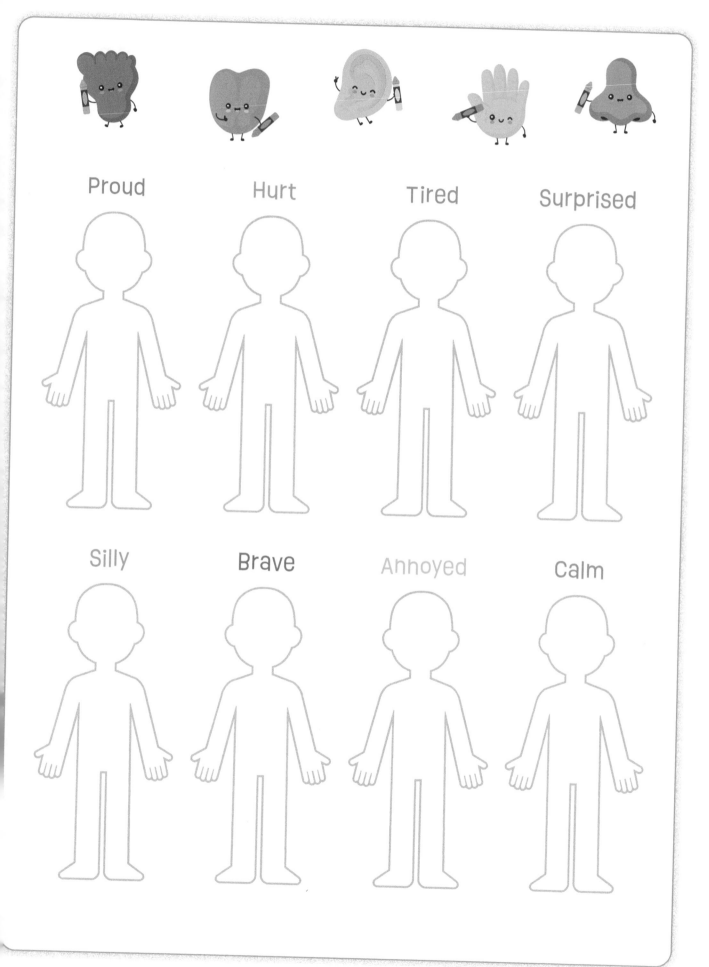

Proud

Hurt

Tired

Surprised

Silly

Brave

Annoyed

Calm

My Body Sensations After EMDR

Color and draw how your body feels now, after you have reached a SUD of 1 or 0 during your EMDR session. During this step of EMDR therapy, we want to make sure that your thoughts, feelings, and body sensations all match and feel better.

Matching My Heart, Mind, and Body

Use this worksheet to explore how you are feeling, what you are thinking, and what you are sensing in your body after you reach a SUD of 1 or 0 at the end of an EMDR session. During this step of EMDR therapy, we want to make sure that your thoughts, feelings, and body sensations all match and feel better. With your EMDR therapist, you may do more back-and-forth movement as needed.

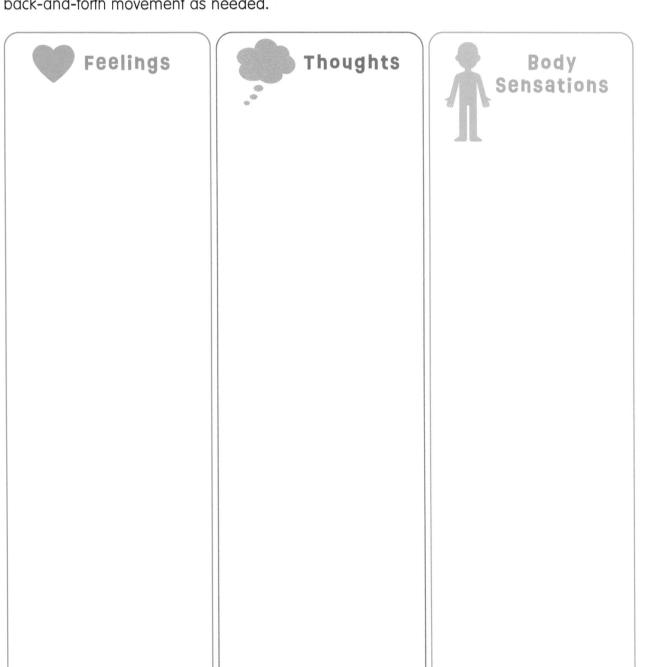

♥ Feelings	💭 Thoughts	Body Sensations

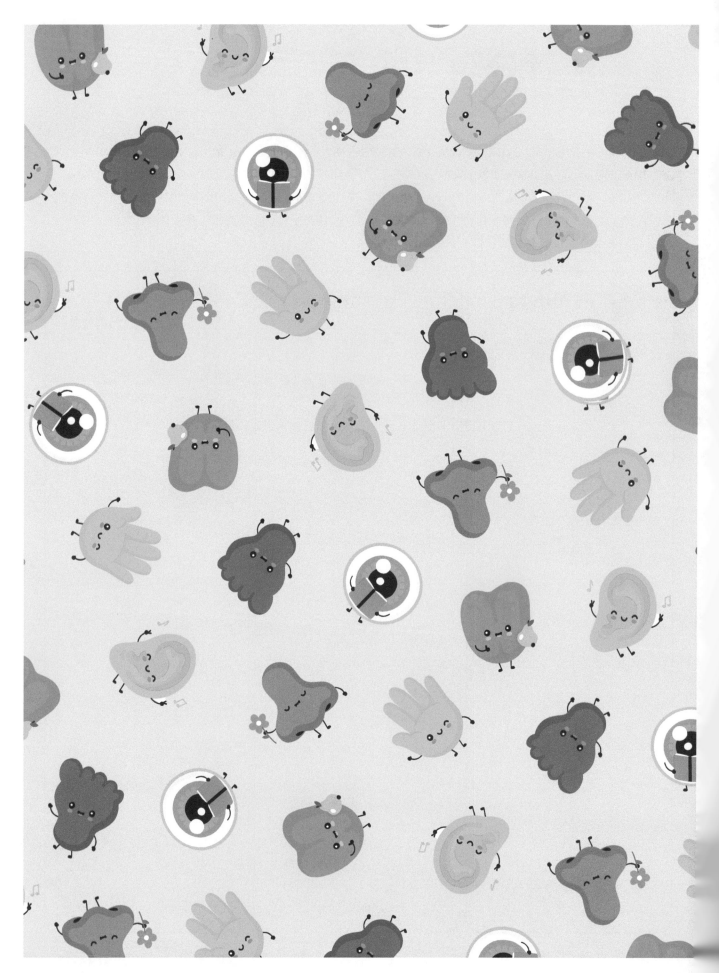

CHAPTER 7

PHASE 7: Finishing and Ending

The goal at the end of every EMDR therapy session is to feel better than you did before. That's why during phase 7 of EMDR, your therapist will work with you to do something calming or fun at the end of each session. Francine Shapiro (2018) called this phase "closure."

After you finish an EMDR session, you might feel less stressed out about the problem you were working on. In fact, you might be able to rate your problem a 0 on a scale of 0 to 10. If so, it's time to celebrate! Rating yourself at a 0 means that you have completed working on one of your target problems and it no longer brothers you!

But other times, you might feel the same or even worse about the problem you're working on. This reaction is normal too. If you do end up feeling bad after an EMDR session, be sure to take extra time with your therapist to feel better before you leave.

If you're not able to rate your problem at a 0 at the end of the session, we call that an "incomplete" EMDR session. This is totally okay! All this means is that during your next EMDR session, you will continue to work on the problem. Your brain will keep working in between EMDR sessions to help you feel better, so if you don't immediately feel like your problem is at a 0, you might feel closer to a 0 throughout the week!

For any problems that you *do* complete during EMDR, the next thing you can do is work on a "future template" for this problem. This is just a fancy way of saying that you brainstorm ideas on how you would like to handle this same problem or a similar problem if it comes up for you again (Shapiro, 2018).

The next several worksheets will help you walk through these steps so you can rate how you're feeling at the end of each session, know what to expect between sessions, and come up with future templates in case you run into similar target problems again.

Clinician Tip: It is important to consider each child's schedule, including any upcoming events they might have, to make a cohesive plan of action for EMDR treatment. Be mindful about each child's treatment goals and which target problems may take more than one EMDR session to complete. If a specific target problem will take multiple sessions, ensure that the child has no major events (e.g., a big test at school or a family vacation) during that time.

How Do I Feel After EMDR?

You might feel many different ways after an EMDR session. Below, circle how you feel after your EMDR session.

 I feel a lot worse.

 I feel a little worse.

 I feel the same.

 I feel a little better.

 I feel a lot better!

What to Expect Between Sessions

There are several things that may happen between EMDR sessions. Over the next week, notice if you experience any of these things and be sure to let your EMDR therapist know the next time you meet.

Feeling better

Feeling worse

More dreams

More nightmares

You remember other memories

You feel more emotional

A problem bothers you more

No problem!

A problem bothers you less

You feel more energized

Yawn!

You feel tired or sleepy

You have a hard time focusing

You have more focus

References: Shapiro (2018) and Beckley-Forest & Monaco (2021)

EMDR Future Template Instructions

This worksheet will help you create something called the "future template." Your EMDR therapist will help you brainstorm how you would like to positively respond in the future to the same problem or similar situations.

1. Identify a similar problem or situation that you might have in the future.

2. Imagine how you will positively respond in the future to this problem or situation.

3. Write down the helpful thought (positive cognition) you have for yourself when you can positively respond to this future problem or situation.

4. Write or draw the positive feelings you get when you positively respond to a future problem or situation.

5. Circle how true your helpful thought feels on a scale of 1 to 7 (where 1 = "completely false" and 7 = "completely true"). Your EMDR therapist may ask you to add back-and-forth movement to help make this thought feel truer.

6. Pretend that you are watching a mini movie of yourself. Imagine watching yourself positively responding to a future problem or situation while thinking your helpful thought. What do you look like? What do you do? What do you say? Do back-and-forth movements with your EMDR therapist to strengthen any positive feelings, thoughts, and body sensations you get from your movie.

7. Optional: With your EMDR therapist, come up with more challenging situations that might come up in the future, and talk about how you can still positively respond.

Reference: Shapiro (2018)

EMDR Future Template Worksheet

 **1.** Future situation

 **2.** Image of future situation

 3. Helpful thought

4. Write or draw your positive feelings

VOC
5. How true is your helpful thought?

| 1 | 2 | 3 | 4 | 5 | 6 | 7 |

 6. Movie of future situation

7. Challenging situations: write or draw how you would respond!

Reference: Shapiro (2018)

CHAPTER 8

PHASE 8: Reviewing and Revising

Hooray! You have made it to the last phase of EMDR therapy. During phase 8, we will review if your problems are getting better or worse. Francine Shapiro calls this phase "reevaluation."

After an EMDR therapy session, some kids have more energy, while other kids feel very tired. Other children experience more dreams or nightmares. Some kids start feeling better right away, while others feel worse at first. Your EMDR therapist will always check in with you to see how things are going at the beginning of each session. They will ask you questions to figure out what has been going well and what hasn't been going so well. If it feels like any of your problems are getting worse, you may work with your therapist to update your treatment plan and goals.

At the start of each session, your therapist will help you review any triggers that you experienced over the past week that caused you to feel uncomfortable thoughts, emotions, or body sensations. A trigger is anything that brings up memories of the scary or traumatic event that happened to you in the past. A good way to track your triggers throughout the week is to use a TICES log, which can help you remember experiences where you felt triggered. At your next EMDR therapy session, this log can be used to identify new targets or roadblocks that might need to be added to your treatment goals.

Clinician Tip: Get crafty with the TICES logs by creating special journals, folders, or binders that the logs can be kept in. Use puppets, stuffed animals, toys, or a sand tray to help children review how things have been for them since the last EMDR session.

What Did You Notice?

Did you notice any changes about your target problem since your last EMDR session? Circle what you noticed, or write or draw what you noticed below.

| Feeling better | Feeling worse | More dreams | More nightmares | You remember other memories | You feel more emotional |

| A problem bothers you more | A problem bothers you less | You feel more energized | You feel tired or sleepy | You have a hard time focusing | You have more focus |

Write or draw other things you noticed below.

TICES Log

Use this log to track your triggers between EMDR sessions. Write down what triggered you, what picture or image came to mind when you were triggered, any thoughts or emotions that you experienced, any body sensations you felt, and how much it bothered you on the SUD scale (0 = "no stress at all" and 10 = "the most stress you could ever feel").

Trigger	📷 Picture	💭 Thoughts	😊 Emotions	🧍 Body Feeling	SUDS (0–10)

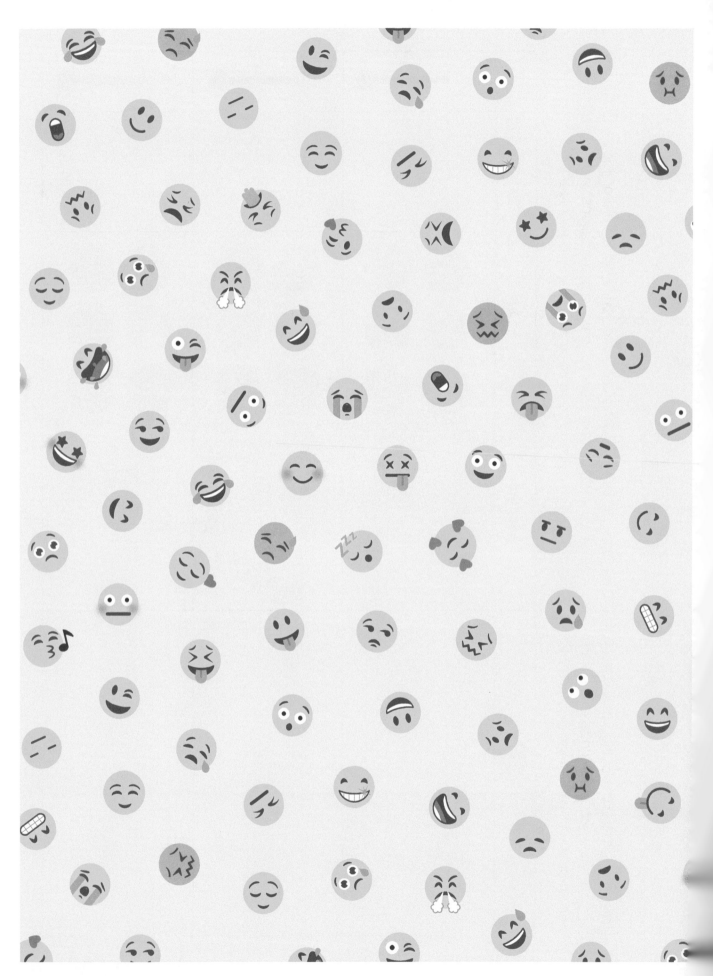

CHAPTER 9

Better Together With Parents and Caregivers

It's a good idea to share information about EMDR therapy with the grown-up who is caring for you. That way, they will understand what EMDR is and what might happen before, during, or after therapy. The more information they have, the better they will be able to help you. The following section includes worksheets and handouts that your caregiver can complete on their own to better help you in therapy. It also includes activities and games that you can do together with your grown-up. Be sure to share these with them so they can support you during your EMDR journey.

Clinician Tip: While it is ideal for parents and caregivers to be involved in EMDR therapy treatment with their child, it may not always be appropriate, depending on the child's situation. For example, if you are working with children in the child welfare or foster care system, consider whether it will be helpful or harmful to include parents and caregivers in EMDR sessions. It is important to always assess if joint EMDR therapy is appropriate and to determine both the child's and the caregiver's readiness.

Phase 1
Your Child's Story and Goals

During phase 1 of EMDR therapy, your EMDR therapist will work with you and your child to gather historical information needed to create a plan and treatment goals for therapy. Your therapist will engage you and your child in several assessments to identify the severity of the problem. Then they will work with you to develop a treatment plan that defines the specific targets on which to use EMDR:

- The event(s) from the past that created the problem

- The present situations that cause distress

- The key skills or behaviors your child needs to learn for their future well-being

It is helpful to keep in mind that sometimes your therapy goal may be different from your child's therapy goal. Your EMDR therapist will work with you as a family to help identify age-appropriate and family-appropriate goals.

Your Child's Story and Your Goals

Please complete this form to help us learn more about your child's story and share about your goals for EMDR therapy.

What are the main concerns for your child?

_____

_____

_____

_____

What goals do you wish to have for your child during EMDR therapy?

_____

_____

_____

_____

When did your child's problems or symptoms begin?

_____

_____

_____

_____

What are some scary, confusing, or traumatic experiences for your child? List them below.

_____

_____

_____

_____

Does your child become triggered by people, places, or things? If so, list your child's triggers below.

_____

_____

_____

_____

What are your child's strengths?

_____

_____

_____

_____

What are your child's interests and hobbies?

_____

_____

_____

_____

What else is important to know about your child?

_____

_____

_____

_____

Phase 2
Helping Your Child Prepare

During phase 2 of EMDR therapy, your EMDR therapist will work with you and your child to build trust, explain how EMDR therapy works, and let you know what to expect during and after an EMDR therapy session. During this phase, you and your child will learn coping skills and calming strategies to handle intense emotions and body sensations they may experience during EMDR therapy.

These techniques are important tools that people of all ages benefit from. The happiest people in the world have many ways of relaxing and decompressing from uncomfortable experiences. One of the goals in EMDR therapy is to make sure that the people who engage in the therapy can take care of themselves.

Strengthening Connections

Sometimes, kids can experience upsetting, scary, and confusing things when they are hurt by a caregiver or another adult in their life. If your traumatic memory involved being hurt by a grown-up, it makes sense that you might feel confused or have mixed feelings about some adults in your life.

Strengthening the relationships you have with the safe and supportive grown-ups in your life can help you heal from these past upsetting experiences. The next set of worksheets, games, and activities will help you and your caregiver create a closer bond and help you better communicate with each other.

Love Messages

In this activity, your caregiver will do most of the work! Your grown-up will answer the questions below to create love messages for you. The only thing you will need to do is pick your favorite back-and forth movement to do *slowly* as you listen to your grown-up share their messages with you. Try to notice what feelings and body sensations you have when you hear your grown-up share their love messages!

What are the things that you love most about your child?

What are your favorite memories of your child?

What do you love to do together with your child?

What are your positive hopes and dreams for your child?

Adapted from Wesselmann et al. (2015)

Singing Songs

In this activity, your grown-up will fill in the blanks to change the words of some popular songs just for you! Your grown-up will sing the song to you with the new words. Your job will be to listen and do your favorite back-and-forth movement slowly as your grown-up sings the tune. It might be a fun idea to use musical instruments to do your back-and-forth movement in this activity! Your grown-up can also do the back-and-forth movements to you (e.g., tapping on your knees or shoulders) or with you!

My Star
(Tune of "Twinkle, Twinkle, Little Star")

(Child's name), (Child's name), my little star,
do you know how great you are?

You are _____ and
you are _____.
You are _____ and
you are _____.

(Child's name), (Child's name), my little star,
oh, I love how great you are!

Sunshine
(Tune of "You Are My Sunshine")

You are my sunshine, my only sunshine.

You make me happy when skies are gray.

You'll never know, dear, how much
I love you. You are _____ and
_____ and
_____.

Here to Keep You Safe
(Tune of "The Wheels on the Bus")

(Caregiver's name) is here to keep you safe,
keep you safe, keep you safe.

(Caregiver's name) is here to keep you safe—
all the time!

(Caregiver's name) is here to hold you tight . . .

(Caregiver's name) is here to tickle you . . .

(Caregiver's name) is here to laugh with you . . .

(Caregiver's name) is here to give you hugs . . .

(Caregiver's name) is here to _____ . . .

Happy
(Tune of "If You're Happy and You Know It")

I am happy today because of you.

I am happy today because of you.

You are _____. You are _____.

You are _____. You are _____.

I am happy today because of you!

**All of the songs above can be repeated multiple times and filled with different words!
Can you think of other popular songs to change the words to?**

Adapted from Wesselmann et al. (2015)

Magical Cord of Love

In this exercise, you will get to pick a color for the "magical cord of love" that connects you and your grown-up. As your grown-up reads this script, use your imagination to picture this magical cord of love. It is best if your grown-up can do slow back-and-forth movements to you as they read the script, like tapping on your hands, shoulders, or knees. You can also sit close to your grown-up while doing your own slow back-and-forth movement.

Grown-Up Script

There is a magical sparkling (color your child chose) cord that stretches and stretches so you are always connected to me and my love never stops.

Even if I am on the moon or (somewhere very far away), the love can stretch and stretch and you are still completely connected.

When I am at (name a place you go often), or if you are at school, you are always in my heart and on my mind.

I love you just the same and my love for you does not stop.

When I am busy with (name something you might be doing, such as taking care of another child, talking on the phone, or talking to another adult), our magical cord still connects us and my love for you does not change.

Even when I feel frustrated or angry with you, the magical cord of love does not fade or lose its power.

I still love you very much even though I am feeling that way.

The magical cord of love stretches and connects us all the time, no matter what.

When I am far away from you, when I am busy with other things, when I feel upset, I love you and you will always be connected to me.

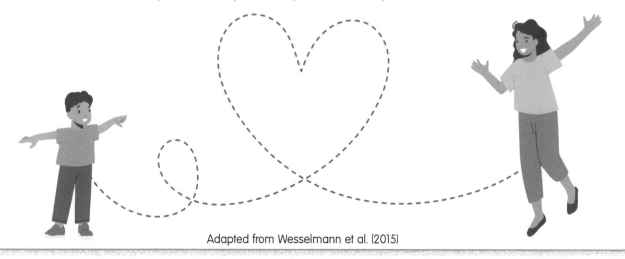

Adapted from Wesselmann et al. (2015)

Circle of Caring

With your EMDR therapist and grown-up, think about all the people who care about you and write their names in the circle below. This list can include grown-ups, other kids, family members, teachers, neighbors, or professionals who help you. With your eyes closed or open, use your imagination to picture all of these people in the room with you. Imagine them surrounding you with their love and care. Imagine their love is a beautiful shimmering color floating around you like glitter floating in the air. As you do this exercise, your grown-up can also do slow back-and-forth movements to you, such as tapping your shoulders, hands, or knees.

Adapted from Wesselmann et al. (2015)

Activating Your Child's Target Problems

During phase 3 of EMDR therapy, the EMDR therapist will ask your child a standard set of questions to activate the target memory or problem that will be addressed during the therapy session. The therapist will then identify the images, negative thoughts, emotions, stress level, and body sensations connected to your child's target problem. They'll also ask what positive thoughts your child would like to have instead, as well as how true those positive thoughts feel.

You will sometimes need to support your child in this phase, especially if they were very young when the trauma occurred or if it is too overwhelming for them to talk about their target problem. You may work with your child's EMDR therapist to create a story for your child to process what has happened to them. The following pages include storytelling guidelines that can be used during joint therapy sessions with your child.

Storytelling Guidelines

When something traumatic has happened to your child, it may be challenging for them to share their story. Your child may have been too young to remember the incident, or it may simply be too stressful for them to talk about. The storytelling technique, originally created by Joan Lovett, can be helpful in the EMDR therapy process with your child. This technique allows you to become a storyteller who creates a narrative that your child can use to process what happened to them. The following guidelines and worksheet will help you create a narrative for your child. Your child's EMDR therapist can also support you in creating this story.

Guidelines for Creating the Story

1. The story is written prior to the EMDR session so that you can be present and focused on your child's emotional response.

2. The story is written from the perspective of your child.

3. The story is told in a fairy-tale format, in third person, with the main character having similar qualities to your child (e.g., similar age, hobbies, dislikes).

4. The story will include your best guess for your child's unhelpful thought (e.g., I am not safe, I am dumb, I am bad) and helpful thought (e.g., I am safe, I am smart, I am a good kid) for the traumatic memory.

5. The story will include a beginning, a middle, and an end. The beginning of the story will focus on your child's strengths. The middle of the story will include details of the traumatic event and your child's unhelpful thought. The end of the story will provide a happy ending—how your child overcame the traumatic event and the helpful thought they have now.

6. Provide your story to the EMDR therapist prior to the therapy session for possible suggestions and adjustments.

7. During the EMDR therapy session, you and your child will decide on what type of back-and-forth movement you'd like to use while you tell the story. The most commonly used back-and-forth movement is to tap on your child's

Adapted from Lovett (1999)

hands, shoulders, knees, or toes while you look at them. You can also have your child sit in your lap and use the butterfly hug. Use whatever type of back-and-forth movement is most comfortable for you and your child during the storytelling.

8. Before you begin telling the story, let your child know that the story will have a happy ending.

9. Remind your child that they may use their stop sign if they want to take a break or if they get out of their zone. You can choose to use a stop sign if you get out of your zone too!

10. There are several other techniques that can be added to enhance the storytelling technique during a joint EMDR session. For example, after you are finished sharing the story, you can ask your child what their favorite part was. If your child shares something positive, you can do additional back-and-forth movements with your child to strengthen this positive resource. You can also ask your child how they could make the story better, including what the character in the story might have been feeling or thinking. After updating the story with your child's input, you can retell the story and apply additional back-and-forth movement. You can also use toys or props in the therapy office to tell the story and do back-and-forth movement.

Adapted from Lovett (1999)

Storytelling Worksheet

The Beginning (This section includes your child's strengths, positive supports, and experiences.)

Once upon a time, there was a _____ named _____.
(Pick one: child, animal, or magical creature)   (Different name from your child's)

_____ lived with _____.
(Main character's name)   (Types of relatives your child lives with, like parents, siblings, or grandparents)

_____ was really good at _____.
(Main character's name)   (Your child's strengths)

They loved to spend time _____.
(Hobbies your child enjoys)

The Middle (This section includes details about your child's traumatic experience.)

One day, a _____ thing happened to _____.
(Pick one: scary, confusing, unfair, sad, or hard-to-understand)   (Main character's name)

_____.
(Describe the traumatic event using all five senses if possible)

_____.

_____ began to think _____.
(Main character's name)   (Unhelpful thought)

and felt _____. As the scary thing was
(List 1–3 negative emotions or feelings your child may have felt)

happening, their body _____.
(List 2–4 body sensations your child may have felt during the traumatic experience)

Since the _____ thing happened, _____
(Scary, confusing, unfair, sad, or hard-to-understand)   (Main character's name)

has had trouble with _____.
(List 2–3 things your child has trouble with, like sleeping, nightmares, or feeling scared)

The End (This section includes a resolution for your child's traumatic experience.)

Ever since the _____ thing happened, _____
(Scary, confusing, unfair, sad, or hard-to-understand)   (Main character's name)

has felt better when _____.
(List 1–3 things that have helped your child cope or feel better)

They know that they have the support of _____.
(List of people or things that can help them if they become triggered)

_____ has learned that _____ and
(Main character's name)   (Helpful thought)

now they can begin to _____.
(What can your child begin doing now that the traumatic experience does not bother them)

And they lived happily ever after.

The End.

Discharging Your Child's Stress

During phase 4, your child's EMDR therapist will have your child focus on the selected target memory or problem while engaging in a series of back-and-forth movements, which is known as bilateral stimulation.

Bilateral stimulation can involve moving the eyes, tapping the hands, marching the feet, using handheld buzzers, or listening to sounds in an alternating pattern. Your child will focus on the target problem while engaging in these bilateral movements to discharge or disconnect from any maladaptive information that is causing distress. The goal is to help your child become desensitized to the target problem so it no longer bothers them.

DISCONNECT & DISCHARGE all the bad stuff

Buzz!

Back and Forth Together

Did you know that you can do back-and-forth movement with the help of the supportive grown-ups in your life? Here are some ideas for back-and-forth movements you can do together. Draw a star in the box for each back-and-forth movement that you are able to practice!

Sit across from your grown-up and have them move a finger puppet or toy back and forth in front of your eyes.

Use TheraTappers or "Buzzies" that vibrate back and forth as you sit next to your grown-up or in their lap.

Sit next to your grown-up or in their lap as they hold your hand to scribble back and forth together on a piece of paper.

Stand up and hold your grown-up's hand while shaking your hips from side to side.

Pick a body part for your grown-up to tap back and forth on, like your head, shoulders, knees, or toes!

Play pat-a-cake with your grown-up to create back-and-forth movement with your hands.

Create your own back-and-forth movement to do together with your grown-up! Write or draw it below.

Create your own back-and-forth movement to do together with your grown-up! Write or draw it below.

Strengthening Your Child's Positive Beliefs

The goal of phase 5 is to strengthen the positive thoughts your child wants to have more of—and for your child to feel that these positive thoughts are completely true.

Imagine that we are deleting the negative thoughts associated with the target problem, and uploading and installing new positive thoughts. For example, your child may initially have the negative thought "I am not good enough." Once your child has successfully reprocessed their target problem, the positive thought "I am good enough" will feel truer!

I am good enough!

STRENGTHEN
&
UPLOAD
all the good stuff

I've Got Your Back Instructions

1. You and your grown-up will take turns drawing invisible letters on the other person's back that spell out a positive quality or trait.

2. The person who is being drawn on will guess the letters and the word being written.

3. Once the word is guessed correctly, use the following worksheet to strengthen this quality.

4. Have the person who wrote the word share a story or memory of a time the other person showed this quality.

5. Do 8 to 10 slow back-and-forth movements after each story or memory is shared.

I've Got Your Back Worksheet

Child: _____   Grown-Up: _____

1. What word was written on your back?

1. What word was written on your back?

2. As you do back-and-forth movements of your choice, listen to your grown-up share a memory of a time when you had this quality.

2. As you do back-and-forth movements of your choice, listen to your child share a memory of a time when you had this quality.

3. What emotions do you feel when you think about the word that was written on your back? Write or draw your emotions below.

3. What emotions do you feel when you think about the word that was written on your back? Write or draw your emotions below.

4. What body sensations do you feel when you think about the word that was written on your back? Color them in the body to the right.

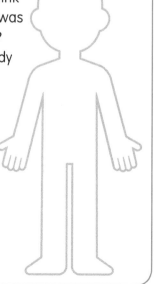

4. What body sensations do you feel when you think about the word that was written on your back? Color them in the body to the right.

Phase 6
Increasing Your Child's Body Awareness

During phase 6 of EMDR therapy, your child will be asked to check in with their body as they think about the target memory and positive cognition.

The goal of this phase is to identify any physical tension or uncomfortable body sensations that still remain (e.g., upset stomach, muscle tension, headache). If any tension remains in the body, they will continue engaging in back-and-forth movements to help discharge this tension from the body.

INCREASE
body awareness

Helping with Ouches Instructions

When you fall and scrape your knee, it's obvious to your grown-up where you are hurting. But sometimes you can have hurts in places that others don't see. For example, you might have a tummy ache, or your heart may feel funny.

In this activity, your grown-up will help you put bandages on places where you feel "ouches" when you think about the upsetting, scary, or traumatic thing that happened to you. First, draw or color the body on the next page to represent you. Then write down the memories that are hurting you in the bubbles on the left below. Next, cut out the colored bandages and tell your grown-up where you feel an "ouch" when you think about that memory. Put the bandages on the body to show all the places that you feel an "ouch."

To learn other creative ways you can do this activity, see the *Helping with Ouches Bonus Ideas* page!

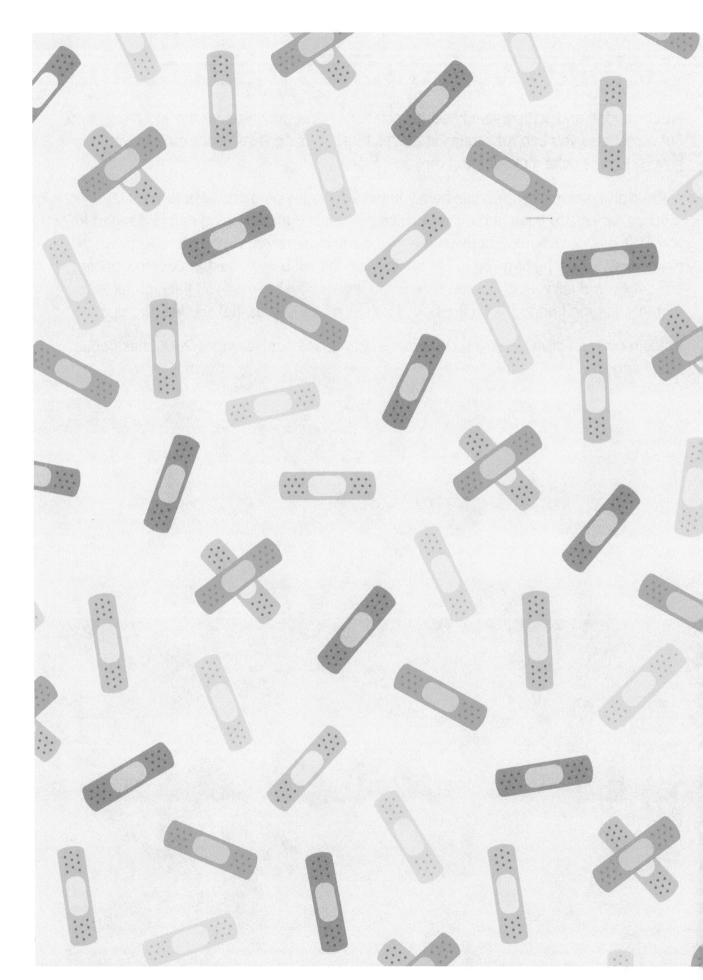

Helping with Ouches Body

Helping with Ouches
Bonus Ideas

There are a lot of other ways to share and learn about where you have "ouches" in your body when you think about scary, upsetting, or traumatic memories. Here are a few more ideas you and your grown-up can try.

Place real bandages or stickers on your own body. For each memory, tell your grown-up where a bandage or sticker needs to be placed.

Do the activity with your favorite stuffed animal or doll. Let your grown-up know where they should put a bandage or sticker for each "ouch."

Find a huge piece of paper (or tape multiple pieces together to form one huge one) and lie down on it. Have your grown-up trace the outline of your body. Let your grown-up know where each "ouch" is located and place bandages, stickers, or sticky notes in each location.

Take this activity outside! Find a place where you can safely lie down and have your grown-up trace an outline of your body using chalk. Then use the chalk or find things in nature, such as rocks or leaves, to be your bandages. Let your grown-up know where you feel an "ouch" so they can place a nature bandage there.

You can also ask your EMDR therapist how to use back-and-forth movements during a joint session to strengthen any positive connections that are made during this activity.

Phase 7

Helping Your Child
Finish and End

The goal at the end of each EMDR therapy session is to help your child feel accomplished and in control. If necessary, your EMDR therapist will engage your child in coping and calming activities during this phase. You can help your child regulate after an EMDR session by doing fun or calm activities with them as well. During this phase, your EMDR therapist will also let you and your child know what to expect between sessions, including any ongoing processing that may occur.

I'm in control of the EMDR game!

Closely Connecting

After each EMDR therapy session, your child may have various responses and reactions for one to two days. Sometimes your child may feel better and calmer, and other times your child may experience negative emotions. Here are examples of responses and reactions your child may display:

- ⭐ Becoming overly talkative
- ⭐ Becoming tired or feeling exhausted
- ⭐ Voicing somatic complaints (e.g., feeling sick, having headaches or stomachaches)
- ⭐ Exhibiting regressed behavior and acting younger than their age
- ⭐ Experiencing nightmares or vivid dreams
- ⭐ Remembering other memories
- ⭐ Acting clingy or scared and feeling like something "bad" will happen
- ⭐ Emotion dysregulation (e.g., temper tantrums, excessive crying)
- ⭐ Expressing that "something feels wrong" or "something doesn't feel right"
- ⭐ Telling you "I don't want to go back to therapy"
- ⭐ Experiencing difficulty concentrating or feeling confused
- ⭐ Speaking as though they are in a fog and spacing out

It's important to create a calm and relaxing environment for your child after an EMDR session. While it may be concerning to see your child regress, most children are back to normal (and better) in a day or two. Here are some ideas to connect with your child and create a caring and relaxing space:

- ⭐ Give your child hugs and other soothing touch (e.g., touching their hair, rubbing their back)
- ⭐ Listen to music together and have a dance party
- ⭐ Let your child relax, rest, watch television, or play video games
- ⭐ Prepare your child's favorite meal or snack for them
- ⭐ Hold your child or let them sit close to you
- ⭐ Praise your child for doing a good job in therapy and tell them you are proud of them
- ⭐ Color or create art together
- ⭐ Read books
- ⭐ Make slime or Play-Doh
- ⭐ Take your child to the park
- ⭐ Go on a bike ride
- ⭐ Watch a movie together
- ⭐ What other calm or fun activity ideas do you have?

Adapted from Beckley-Forest & Monaco (2021)

Phase 8

Helping Your Child Review and Revise

During follow-up EMDR sessions, your child's EMDR therapist will check in about how your child has adjusted after the last session. It will be important to note if there have been any significant changes in symptoms or behaviors in your child. The following pages will provide you with more guidance to collect information after an EMDR session.

Collecting Information

Over the next week, notice how your child is feeling, thinking, and behaving after each EMDR therapy session. Use the log on the next page to keep track of whether your child is experiencing an increase or decrease in negative or positive thoughts, feelings, behaviors, body sensations, and dreams or memories. You may choose to do this independently or with your child; you are also encouraged to do a combination of both!

Remember, it is easier to pay attention to regressed behaviors, but it is also important to notice improved behaviors. It is a good thing if there are fewer experiences of unwanted or unhealthy behaviors!

Post-EMDR Session Log

+/- Thoughts	+/- Feelings	+/- Behaviors	+/- Body Sensations	+/- Dreams or Memories

Adapted from Beckley-Forest & Monaco (2021)

Post-EMDR Session Log

+/- Thoughts	+/- Feelings	+/- Behaviors	+/- Body Sensations	+/- Dreams or Memories

Parent/Caregiver Reevaluation Questions

After you and your child left the EMDR therapy session, how was your child that night? Was your child more energetic? Quiet? Withdrawn? Take note!

During the week:

⭐ Did your child have any issues with sleep over the past week? Did they wake up in the middle of the night? Did they have trouble falling asleep? Did they have dreams or nightmares? Was there any bedwetting?

⭐ Did your child's behaviors get better, stay the same, or become worse? Was your child able to follow the rules better at home?

⭐ Did your child have moments of cooperation? Were they kind to siblings or pets?

⭐ Did they have any physical symptoms after the session (or during the week) that were out of the norm? Stomach issues? Headaches?

⭐ Did they have any temper tantrums? Did the temper tantrums last as long as they normally do, shorter, or longer? Was your child more irritable, annoyed, or angry? Or did these symptoms decrease?

⭐ Was your child more tearful, sad, or upset? Or did these symptoms decrease?

⭐ Was your child more clingy, anxious, or worried? Or did these symptoms decrease?

⭐ Was your child more scared, depressed, or withdrawn? Or did these symptoms decrease?

⭐ Did you receive any calls or notes from your child's school this week? What did they report?

⭐ Did your child interact with their friends better, about the same, or worse over the past week?

⭐ Did your child share more memories or talk about things that bothered them more?

⭐ Are there new events that have happened in the family that would be important for your EMDR therapist to know? This can include a loss in the family, graduation, travel, parent separation, missed parent visitation, and so forth.

Adapted from Beckley-Forest & Monaco (2021)

Helping Your Child Reevaluate

Help your child write down the problems they are currently experiencing. Examples of problems your child may describe include having nightmares, feeling worried, getting scared, or feeling angry. Make a copy of this worksheet and help your child graph the severity of their problems each week to show if any problems are worsening or improving.

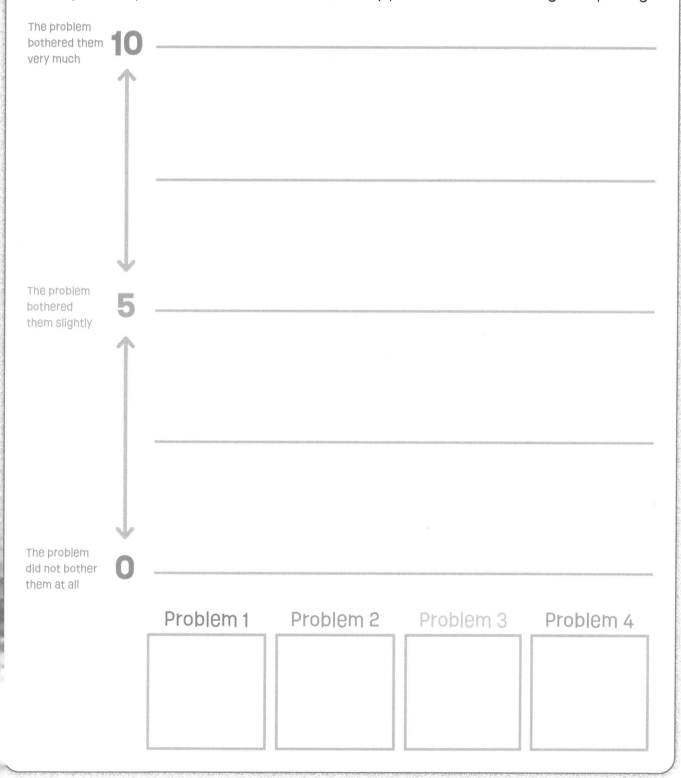

The problem bothered them very much **10**

The problem bothered them slightly **5**

The problem did not bother them at all **0**

Problem 1	Problem 2	Problem 3	Problem 4

References

Adler-Tapia, R., & Settle, C. (2008). *EMDR and the art of psychotherapy with children*. Springer.

Artigas, L., Jarero, I., Mauer, M., López Cano, T., & Alcalá, N. (2000, September). *EMDR and traumatic stress after natural disasters: Integrative treatment protocol and the butterfly hug*. Poster presented at the EMDRIA Conference, Toronto, Ontario, Canada.

Beckley-Forest, A., & Monaco, A. (2021). *EMDR with children in the play therapy room: An integrated approach*. Springer.

Cannon, W. B. (1915). *Bodily changes in pain, hunger, fear, and rage: An account of recent researches into the function of emotional excitement*. Appleton-Century-Crofts.

Gomez, A. M. (2013). *EMDR therapy and adjunct approaches with children: Complex trauma, attachment, and dissociation*. Springer.

Korn, D. L., & Leeds, A. M. (2002). Preliminary evidence of efficacy for EMDR resource development and installation in the stabilization phase of treatment of complex posttraumatic stress disorder. *Journal of Clinical Psychology, 58*(12), 1465–1487.

Kuypers, L. (2011). *The zones of regulation: A curriculum designed to foster self-regulation and emotional control*. Think Social Publishing.

Lovett, J. (1999). *Small wonders: Healing childhood trauma with EMDR*. Free Press.

Shapiro, F. (2018). *Eye movement desensitization and reprocessing (EMDR) therapy: Basic principles, protocols, and procedures* (3rd ed.). Guilford Press.

Siegel, D. (1999). *The developing mind: How relationships and the brain interact to shape who we are*. Guilford Press.

Wesselmann, D., Schweitzer, C., & Armstrong, S. (2015). Child attachment trauma protocol. In M. Luber (Ed.). *Eye movement desensitization and reprocessing (EMDR) therapy scripted protocols and summary sheets: Treating trauma- and stressor-related conditions* (pp. 9–43). Springer.